The S'
on
Pilgrim Street

by

Joan Histon

Hickory
Tree
Press.
Whickham

Other publications by Hickory Tree Press:

1. Happy Days & Homework
A History of Hookergate School 1932-1970
by Alan Wright (1991)
ISBN 0-9519-6260-4 (pbk)

2. Coal, Community & Conflict
A History of Chopwell
by Kathryn Hordon & Alan Wright (1995)
ISBN 0-9519-6261-2 (pbk)

3. Energy, Exergy & Entropy
A History of International Research & Development Co. Ltd
by Alan Wright (1996)
ISBN 0-9519-6262-0 (pbk)

4. To Reason Why.....
by Bill Brough (2001)
ISBN 0-9519-6263-9 (pbk)

Another local history publication published by Reyrolle Heritage Trust Press, Hebburn:
Arcs, Sparks & Engineers
A Centenary History of A. Reyrolle & Co. Ltd (1901-2001)
by Alan Wright (Ed.) (2001)
ISBN 0-9538972-0-6 (hdbk)
ISBN 0-9538972-1-4 (pbk)

Published by Hickory Tree Press
c/o, 41 Cherrytree Drive, Whickham, Newcastle upon Tyne. NE16 4TQ
email: hickorytp@lineone.net
Published 2002
Text copyright: Joan Histon
Front cover: Photograph courtesy of The Bible House
Back cover: Photograph courtesy of The Bible House.

Printed by: Sovereign Press (Printers), Split Crow Road, Gateshead, Tyne & Wear.

ISBN 0-9519-6264-7

British Library Cataloguing-in-Publication Data.
A catalogue for this book is available from the British Library.

ACKNOWLEDGEMENTS

I would like to take this opportunity to thank the following people who have used their memories and expertise to make this book possible:

Anne Hedley
Alan Jessup
Beryl Johnson
Roger & Jean Middleton
Edith Quick
Alan Wright
The Trustees and staff of The Bible House

In addition to The Bible House archives I used the following book for source material on the Bainbridge family:

The Bainbridges of Newcastle - A Family History 1679-1976
by Angela & John Airey (1979).

Finally, I would also like to thank Colin, my husband, for his encouragement and constructive criticism and my friend Sue, for praying me through every step of the way.

Joan Histon

Also by Joan Histon:
Thy Will Be Done....Eventually!
by Alex Annand & Joan Histon (1999)
ISBN 1-85852-140-8
Published by Methodist Publishing House.

The Main Players.

Thomas H. Bainbridge (1847-1912). Son of the founder of Bainbridge and Co., formerly of Market Street, Newcastle. Lifetime supporter and patron of numerous charities in Newcastle. Trustee of The Bible & Tract Depot. Married Kate Benson. Lindsay Bainbridge (1882-1915) and Wilfred Bainbridge (1884-1919) were two of his sons.

George B. Bainbridge (1850-1944). Younger brother of Thomas. Trustee.

Ian Clarkson. A colporteur employed by the Edinburgh Colporteur Society.

E. J. Crosier. Trustee.

Caroline Dickinson. Employed as shop girl. Married Robert Middleton, the Manager.

Charles Dymond. Trustee.

Gordon Firth. Bank Manager. Trustee.

Jane Gibson. Employed as shop girl. The Bible & Tract Depot possibly paid for her education.

Tom Gibson. A fictitious character.

Hannah & Ruth Grigs. Daughters of Captain Grigs, Master Mariner.

Henry Harris. Assistant Manager of the shop. His daughter, Henrietta, was employed as shop girl.

Rowland Hay. Trustee. Solicitor.

Mr Jacks. A fictitious character.

Janice. A fictitious character.

Beryl Johnson. Current Manageress of The Bible House.

Ephraim Lister. Canvassed for donations/subscriptions, visited publishers and took the Minutes of the Committee Meetings.

Joseph Maher. Trustee and treasurer of The Bible & Tract Depot. It was in his home that several gentlemen met to discuss setting up The Bible and Tract Depot.

Robert Middleton. Served for over fifty years as Manager of The Bible & Tract Depot.

William Middleton. Took over from his father, Robert, as Manager of The Bible & Tract Depot.

Fay Middleton. Daughter of Robert Middleton and Manageress for three years.

Mr Muckle. Trustee.

Albert Peters. Chairman of The Bible House.

Thomas Pumphrey (1833-1911). Son of Quaker parents. Joined his uncle, Henry Richardson, in the grocery business in 1855 in Newcastle. Well known for his coffee shop which opened in 1887 in Cloth Market, Newcastle. Trustee.

Edith Quick. One-time Manageress of The Bible House.

Henry Richardson. Quaker. Was in the Leather Trade. He promoted the establishment of a boys' "ragged school". He and his wife Anna began the first day school, supported by their friends.

David Richardson. Leather Merchant. Trustee.

Elisabeth Smith. Depositary at The Bible & Tract Depot.

William Smythe. Took over the duties of Ephraim Lister.

William Stephens. Manager of Tyne Steam Shipping Co. Supporter of the Temperance Movement and one of the gentlemen who started the Town Moor 'Hoppings' as an antidote to the drinking at the Race Meetings.

Annie Stephenson. Employed as cleaner and occupied the two rooms in the attic.

Mary Jane Stephenson. The Bible & Tract Depot paid for her education and then employed her as shop girl.

Ted Stephenson. A fictitious character.

John Stephenson. A fictitious character.

Margaret Wilson. Depositary. Taught two evenings a week at Manors Evening School for Girls which was run by the Quakers.

Present Trustees. Peter G. Firth (Independent Financial Advisor), David L. Kilner (Chartered Accountant), Peter H. Morley (Solicitor) and David N. Walton (Chartered Accountant).

PART ONE
THE SHOP ON PILGRIM STREET
November 1868

The fog swirled around him, cold and clammy as he made his way unsteadily down the gang-plank. The steam ship hissed and groaned gently behind him. Ephraim Lister was no sailor, never had been. It had taken two days to surge through the heavy North Sea to London, leaving him sick and weak on his arrival and the return journey to Newcastle upon Tyne, had been equally slow and uncomfortable due to a thick blanket of fog covering most of the eastern coast.   Still, business had been good. The Committee would be well pleased! He stepped on to the Quayside with a sigh of relief. It was good to be home. The High Level bridge spanning the River Tyne, loomed black above him in the misty darkness of the early November evening. He remembered it being built twenty years ago when he was just a young lad and the thrill of standing beside his father watching the first steam engine puffing its way across the river. There and then he promised himself that one day he would be in one of those carriages. He would have enjoyed being able to take his business trip to London on the railway instead of by sea. A far more civilised and quicker way of travelling in his opinion, but that would have cost money and money was something the Committee were short of. Besides which, he could hardly have turned down the kind offer of free passage made by Mr William Stevens, the manager of the Steam Shipping Company and friend of the Committee.

Seven o'clock chimed from the belfry of old St. Nicholas Cathedral as Ephraim made his way from the Quayside, through Sandhill. This old part of the city, used by traders and travellers in centuries past, was still a lively commercial centre but at this time of the evening shops were closing after a long hard day. Horses with empty carts stood patiently in the dark waiting for hire, perhaps hoping their load would not be too heavy up the steep ascent leading to Pilgrim Street, one of the oldest parts of the town. Ephraim found the uneven cobbled stones slippery underfoot and the climb soon had him panting, but at least the fog was thinning the further he moved uphill and away from the river.

He took the route through Akenside Hill, and Lower Pilgrim Street, with its rows of overcrowded dingy houses. Here poverty and crime were the rulers and pick-pockets lurked around every dark corner. It was a place where small provision shops and furniture brokers squeezed the last farthing from hungry mothers struggling to make ends meet, because invariably their husbands were in one of the public houses drinking their wages away. He disliked this part of town intensely, because try as he might, he couldn't find his God in poverty stricken situations such as these and this bothered him. It was an unanswered question in his mind and he wasn't one for unanswered questions. He liked things to be in order did Mr Ephriam Lister.

A knot of fear tightened in Ephraim's stomach as a large dark figure loomed out of one of the many narrow side alleys.

'Evening Mr Lister sir.'

Seeing the tall helmet and high collared tunic he breathed a sigh of relief. 'Good evening constable. Cold evening isn't it?'

'It certainly is sir.' The constable gave a salute of respect and slowly ambled down the hill casually swinging his truncheon, his slow steady footsteps echoing reassuringly in Ephraim's ears.

Ephraim stopped to catch his breath. A small dirty, barefooted boy of about eight sat shivering on the steps of one of the tenement dwellings watching him. Ephraim smiled at the solemn face. Even if it was washed it would never be handsome as an ugly red birthmark stretched from his cheek down his neck. The small boy eyed the tall man warily but didn't smile back. Not that he was afraid. The boy thought he had a kindly face, but well-dressed men like him didn't normally smile at you unless they wanted you to run a message and he was too hungry and cold to bother running anywhere tonight, so he just eyed Ephraim suspiciously and stretched out his hand.

'Hev ye got a bit tae spare Mister?' Ephraim thrust his gloved hand into his pocket and bringing out a farthing, dropped it into the grubby palm. 'Thanks Mister.' the boy responded.

Ephraim wasn't a rich man by any stretch of the imagination but he gave what he could afford to the poor. Common sense told him that he couldn't be expected to give much when he had a wife and two children to support, yet he was always left with a feeling of guilt every time he saw young children begging on the streets. The young boy remained seated, watching the man make his way slowly up the hill until he was out of view.

2

Then he returned to his lonely preoccupation of waiting for his mother or sister to arrive home, hoping one of them had managed to buy, beg or even steal some food for their supper.

The road widened as Ephraim reached the upper part of Pilgrim Street. Here stood some goldsmith's shops and rather more select, two storey dwellings. The road continued on into Northumberland Street, with its fashionable three-storey private houses and shops, but Ephraim wasn't going that far. He'd reached his destination. He stood underneath the painted sign, "The Bible and Tract Depot", gazing at the large open bible on display in the shop window. An advertising board hung on the brown front door post announcing meetings for the Temperance Movement, of which most of the Committee were members. It was such an elegant shop. The general assortment of Bibles, prayer books and Sunday School material was artfully displayed and at the back of the shop was the room used as a warehouse and packing room.

Ephraim had been overjoyed when he'd been employed to manage these premises. He had worked hard and was proud of the extensive and varied stock he'd been responsible for building up during his trips to London publishers. The pay wasn't high, only £30 per annum and the hours were long and had to be fitted in with his duties as local agent of the Bible Society, but his general duties were interesting and the Committee had supplied him and his family with accommodation in the two upper rooms and attic over the shop. They charged £10 per annum but much to Mrs Lister's delight that included a stove, chiffoinairre, bookshelves, an upstairs doorbell and free coal, gas and water. The only drawback to the job was the travelling.

The gas lights flickered as cold air entered the shop with him sending shadows dancing across the walls.

'Oh Mr Lister, you're back!' The depositary, Margaret Wilson's greeting was genuine and her brown eyes smiled a welcome into his own. She was a woman in her mid-thirties who struggled to maintain the plainness that her Quaker upbringing demanded. Her hair was pulled tightly back into a bun, but some wilful curls, had escaped during the day, which had the effect of softening and adding an attractiveness to her face.. Like Ephraim Lister, she had thrown herself wholeheartedly into the setting up of the shop. 'Did you have a good journey?' she asked.

'I did not, Miss Wilson but thank you for asking.' Wearily he took off his hat and placed it on the small hat stand by the door. 'Business in London was good and I had plenty opportunity to canvas for donations.' He glanced at his pocket watch. 'It's rather late for you to be still at work isn't it? You should have finished at seven o'clock.'

Margaret Wilson hesitated. 'There were a few problems.' she said.

'Problems?'

'Yes.' Margaret Wilson pushed one of the wilful curls behind her ear.

'The local constable reported seeing some mischievous boys pushing paper in the keyhole of the shop door last night and then trying to light it. The incident was most upsetting! Most upsetting!' Her voice shook. 'Fortunately he chased them away before any serious damage was done, but I've had to spend the best part of the morning scraping what remains of the paper out of the door lock. We were fortunate we didn't have a fire.' She hesitated. 'There was also... er...'

'Yes?'

'We also had a few problems with the water.'

'Water?'

'Yes. Mrs Lister had difficulty carrying the household water up and down the stairs, so I stayed behind to give her a hand. She was wondering if you'd spoken to the Committee about it yet?'

Ephraim sighed. His wife knew this was to be sorted out when he returned from London. Goodness me, why couldn't she have waited? It sounded as though life had been hectic enough for poor Miss Wilson!

'I have.' he said levelly. 'But carrying water is not one of your duties Miss Wilson. You have enough to do and you have not been well of late.' He glanced anxiously at her rather pale face. On more than one occasion he had been forced to manage the shop himself due to her absence from work. 'No doubt you will be pleased to hear the Committee have agreed we should employ a charwoman to clean and carry water to the upper floors for Mrs Lister's household needs. They also suggested employing a shop girl to assist you, especially when I am in London, and an errand girl for delivering books and lighting fires in the shop during the winter months.' He hesitated, 'You wouldn't by any chance know of anyone willing to undertake any of these services would you Miss Wilson?'

Margaret Wilson's head poised thoughtfully to one side. 'There is a girl I used to teach called Hannah Grigs. She's about seventeen. She would make an ideal shop girl.' Margaret Wilson taught young girls every Tuesday

4

and Thursday evening at the Quaker's Friend's Evening School at Manors.

'Of course she's been brought up Baptist,' she added frowning, 'Nevertheless, her father is a very honourable gentleman. A Captain Grigs, Master Mariner. She and her sister Ruth, have run the house for him since their mother died in the cholera epidemic some years ago.'

'Is she looking for employment do you think?'

Margaret Wilson pursed her lips thoughtfully. 'I'll ask shall I?'

'Yes please, Miss Wilson.'

Margaret Wilson lifted her coat from a hook behind the door. 'I shall call tomorrow afternoon while you are looking after the shop Mr Lister. Is there anything else?'

'No Miss Wilson. Thank you for staying behind.'

Margaret Wilson wrapped the coat firmly around herself and pulled on her black bonnet. 'Goodnight sir. I shall see you tomorrow at nine o'clock.'

'Goodnight Miss Wilson.'

After securing the shop door behind her, Ephraim Lister turned off the gas lights and made his way wearily upstairs to his wife, his two sons and his two upper rooms and attic.

******

Ephraim Lister ran his finger around the neck of his collar before making a few notes in the Minutes Book. It was warm in the room. As secretary he had to keep his mind on what was being said but he'd made the mistake of building up the coal fire too high and the gas lamps, which he'd lit due to the unusually dark and dismal morning, made the room feel stuffy. .

There were seven men present out of the thirteen Committee members at this morning's meeting. These were all educated, influential and affluent businessmen working in the city of Newcastle upon Tyne and they had earned Ephraim's deepest respect. Four years ago, in 1864, a group of them, already involved in the British and Foreign Bible Society, the Sunday School Union and the Religious Tract Society, had expressed deep concern over the levels of ignorance and moral wretchedness in the city. Determined to do something about it, they had discussed a venture for opening a shop for the distribution of Bibles, religious tracts, Sunday School material and suitable books for the advancement of Christian knowledge. They estimated that £250 would be required to furnish and stock such premises and had

5

launched an appeal to their various churches for gifts and interest free loans, as well as giving generously themselves. Within a few months the elegant shop at No. 55, Pilgrim Street had been rented and he and Miss Margaret Wilson had been employed.

Unfortunately, much to the shock of everyone gathered at this morning's meeting, a letter had been received from the Corporation advising them that Number 55, Pilgrim Street may not be standing much longer. The Corporation were intending to purchase the shop and adjacent premises with a view to clearing the whole area to form the site for a new Police Station, Court and Fire Station.

'This dreadful problem of having to find new premises to rent is of great concern! Great concern!' Mr Maher's voice carried an anxious note to it. He was treasurer and acting chairman for the morning and it was in his home that The Bible & Tract Depot had become more than an idea but an active part of their lives. 'This, on top of the depression in trade means we are struggling to meet our growing expenses. It is all extremely worrying!'

Thomas Hudson Bainbridge, the youngest of the gentleman gathered that morning, leant across the table. He was a smart young man with fair handsome features. 'Gentlemen, have we no good news to focus on?' All eyes turned upon him, hoping he'd found something positive to rescue them from the deep depression that had descended over the morning's meeting. 'Firstly, we have until next May to find new premises. Surely with all the contacts we have in the city, we'll find something suitable and at an acceptable rent?' There were nods of assent around the table. 'Secondly, with regard to the depression in trade, we are still managing to bring in a fair income. The Town Mission have agreed to pay £5 per annum for the use of our Committee room. Then Rev Scott has offered to supply us with Wesleyan hymnbooks at wholesale prices and thirdly, thanks to Mr Lister, who called on members and friends of the shop during his leisure time, their forthcoming loans and gifts are helping us over a very difficult period.'

His sombre colleagues couldn't help but smile at his enthusiasm, for Thomas was an enthusiast. His Methodist local preaching, church involvement and class leadership at Brunswick Chapel, and even his father's drapery business, Bainbridge & Co., were all run with a strong enthusiastic desire to serve God. Now, at the age of twenty-five, he had become an active member of the Temperance Movement.

'And let us not forget Mr Lister's efforts in managing to obtain 500 copies of a cheap edition of "Pilgrim's Progress" while he was in London.' Mr Henry Richardson spoke quietly for he was a quiet, elderly gentleman, tall and lean with a long gaunt face and pince-nez spectacles perched on the edge of his nose. He was in the leather trade, a member of the Bible Society, an activist in the anti-slavery trade and one of the founders of what was termed "The Ragged School". 'A few copies of "Pilgrims Progress" will be very welcome in our school.'

'Indeed they will sir. Indeed they will!' Mr Maher concurred, catching the positive drift of the conversation. 'However, I do feel, with regard to this question of new premises, that we should be looking for something a little less expensive. Do you agree?' Mr Maher seemed unable to get his mind off money this morning. He shuffled a few papers on the table while the rest of the Committee muttered amongst themselves, before agreeing with a show of hands. Mr Maher surveyed the raised hands approvingly. It was the first time he'd felt remotely happy all morning. 'Well now gentlemen, if there is no further business shall we conclude with prayer?'

As of one accord the men bowed their heads for the regular prayer time that began and ended their meetings and a deep reverence filled the room. 'Oh Holy and most Almighty Father, Thou knowest the problem we have and our need to find new premises urgently.........' (Not half so great a problem as finding new accommodation for me and my family, thought Ephraim worriedly. The news had hit him quite severely that morning and he wondered how his wife would react when he told her. She had a tendency to panic at the best of times.) 'Oh Father. You have led us thus far in our enterprise for You. We beseech You to meet our needs for new premises, financial support and the employment of new staff.' 'Amens!' echoed reverently around the room but none were more reverently, and urgently, uttered than Ephraim's.

Ephraim followed the gentlemen down the stairs, having full confidence in Miss Wilson's ability to greet them with a neat orderly shop but unable to focus his mind on little else but the worrying news that he would have to move. It couldn't have come at a worse time. His children were settled at the church school nearby and Mrs Lister had even announced that once that bothersome water problem was sorted out, she would be contented - and Mrs Lister's contentment meant a great deal to Ephraim Lister - a great deal!

Thomas Bainbridge, had no such worries. Cold and damp the day may be, but he had planned an afternoon fishing on the Coquet River and exploring further his exciting new venture. Once he got his teeth into something he would work tirelessly until his objective had been achieved.

'Cousin Tom! I knew you'd be here so I've come to beg a favour.' The voice belonged to Kate Benson. She swept across the shop floor towards them looking, even in the simplicity of a plain blue cornflower dress, as beautiful as a young woman of twenty could ever look. 'Good morning gentlemen.' She flashed a smile at the members of the Committee, her deep blue eyes somehow managing to include them all, making them feel it was a personal greeting. 'Tom dear, do take me to your father's shop and show me the new line in hats from London.' Her voice was warm, pleading. She tilted her head to one side and auburn curls danced from beneath her bonnet. One glance at Thomas Bainbridge, could see he was totally besotted with his cousin Kate.

'But Kate I was going fishing.' He wasn't *that* besotted!

She pouted prettily at him. 'Oh Tom, please?'

Tom's heart sank.. He had really been looking forward to his fishing trip. He could feel his resolve waver and was annoyed with himself, yet at the same time unable to contain the deep sense of pleasure that an hour or so with Kate gave him. 'Well, I suppose.....'

Kate Benson's lips parted, in a smile, revealing a quirk of humour lurking behind the request. 'Poor Tom. I'm teasing you. I can visit Bainbridge's any time, but I want to see your new Gospel Van. Can I?'

'How do you know about that?' Thomas frowned at her.

'Because you're not very good at keeping new ideas to yourself. Can I come?

Thomas hesitated.

'Please cousin Tom? I won't be in the way. Promise! I may even be of some help?'

The older members of the Committee watched the exchange with some interest. Having Kate Benson around would do Thomas Bainbridge the world of good. It was healthy for a young man to be enthusiastic in his business and church life, but a man needed a partner and a marriage between Kate and Tom would be a good match.

'Well...' Thomas sighed grudgingly and was rewarded by a squeal of delight and a generous hug from his cousin. There were chuckles of amusement from Mr Maher and one or two other eminent members of the Committee.

Mr Henry Richardson did not laugh. He was engrossed in watching a small, dirty figure, staring through the shop window at the gilt-edged Bible standing open in the glass cage. The boy's clothes were almost rags. His thin sharp features were pinched with cold and his thick black hair, badly needed both a wash and cut. The boy's looks weren't improved by the ugly red birth mark that down his cheek and neck. Every so often he turned to beg from passers-by but he appeared more focused on the shop window than on begging. A pang of compassion flooded over Henry Richardson. In fact, every time he came across a poor ignorant child, something inside him cried out to put an end to the ignorance. That was how he and his wife Anna, greatly disturbed by the plight of bare-footed, ragged children wandering the streets of the city, had become involved in establishing the first day school with their Quaker friends.

'Excuse me gentlemen.' As inconspicuously as possible he made his way outside.

John Stephenson didn't see him coming. If he had he would have run away, but he had become totally absorbed in the large book that drew him to this shop window every day. John stared at the words for a long time, then his eyes moved to the picture on the opposite page. A man in a long white gown sat on a rock smiling at a little boy sitting on his knee. Other children gathered around him on the grass, listening fascinated to the story the man appeared to be telling them. His eyes were warm and kind and sometimes in his wildest fantasies, John Stephenson could believe he was the little boy on the man's knee. But that was just a fantasy. Nobody ever offered him anything! Even at the age of eight he had discovered that life was a struggle. He was always hungry and cold and often in pain from the thrashing his father gave him when he came home from the pub and discovered he hadn't made enough money begging on the streets. John Stephenson's friends thought he was daft staring in a book shop window but John didn't care what they thought. He was bored with their stupid games and hurt by their cruel jibes over the appearance of his face. Most of all he was angry with them for filling the keyhole of his special shop with paper and trying to start a fire! That upset him. This shop was unlike the jewellery shop, the bakery and all the other shops along Upper Pilgrim Street. There was something in this particular shop window that he found comforting and there was little enough comfort in John Stephenson's life.

'You seem to like that picture?'

John was startled at the closeness of the voice and cringed back against the window pane.

'I didn't do nowt.'

Henry Richardson stooped down, smiling reassuring at the boy. 'That's my favourite picture as well. Do you like it?'

The boy nodded. Still unsure.

'Do you know who it is?'

The boy shook his head and seeing Henry Richardson wasn't going to scold him, boldly asked, 'Do you?'

'Yes I do. His name is Jesus Christ. Have you heard of Him?'

The boy shook his head and a deep pang of regret washed over Henry Richardson. 'What's your name?'

'John Stephenson.'

'Did I see you begging just now John?'

The boy hesitated, unsure whether he'd get into trouble for begging or whether the man was going to give him money. He decided to take the risk and nodded his head. 'Instead of begging, would you like to learn to read?' he pointed to the book.

John Stephenson stared at Henry Richardson. Then his eyes strayed to the book in the window with the colourful picture he loved and all those words he couldn't read. 'Can y' really teach me t'read?'

'Only if you want to learn and you're willing to work really hard.'

A wide smile broke out across the boy's face. 'Would that mean I could read any'o them books in the shop?' He turned, pressing his face up against the cold pane of glass, his mouth forming pockets of steam on the window.

Henry Richardson patted the boy's tousled head. 'Yes. Any of those books.' he said kindly and waved Margaret Wilson out of the shop to find out more about the young fellow.

******

Margaret Wilson was in a fluster and Margaret Wilson didn't get into a fluster very often. She'd spent the morning sorting out the Committee room for the meeting. Then Miss Kate Benson had arrived on some pretext or other and etiquette demanded she spend time with the lady but she knew

10

that what Miss Kate Benson really wanted was to see Mr Thomas Bainbridge. Then Mr Maher dropped the bombshell that they would have to leave these premises in the none too distant future so she had better think about taking stock of their books. Finally, after Mr Richardson had taken young John Stephenson under his wing, she'd been left to visit his mother, who lived on Lower Pilgrim Street.

After the initial shock of seeing such a nice lady as Miss Wilson in her home, Mrs Stephenson had agreed to allow John to go to what people called, the "Ragged School". Mrs Stephenson had stood over her wash tub listening to Miss Wilson tell her how no less than Mr Henry Richardson himself had seen her John standing outside The Bible & Tract Depot, staring at the books and how he had offered him a place in his school. Of course she didn't dare say no. Not after that nice Miss Wilson had gone to all this trouble. She had even suggested their Mary Jane might like to apply for the job of errand girl in their shop. That would be handy, or at least the extra money would be. But what her husband would have to say about their John doing book learning was quite a different matter. He'd probably say that all that learning would make him too high and mighty, then give him a slap and go down the pub. Hopefully though, he'd be so drunk when he got back he'd have forgotten all about it.

Annie Stephenson stood over her steaming wash tub after Margaret Wilson had left and allowed herself a few minutes to dream. It was something she hadn't done in a long time. She wiped her soapy hands on her pinny. She always felt she hadn't really done a very good job in caring for her family. Three of them she'd lost in the cholera epidemic. Some said it was because raw sewage had been allowed to flow into the water in the city, but all she knew was that over one thousand five hundred people had died and three of those had been her children. Only their Mary Jane had survived.

Ted had started drinking after that and the drink had lost him a number of jobs and brought violence into their home. Then eight years ago, John had been born. She had hoped life would get better when Ted saw he had a son but he'd just seen John as another mouth to feed. Perhaps, just perhaps her John, the quiet dreamer, would be the one to make something of himself. Annie Stephenson smiled a slow quiet smile to herself then determinedly thrust her hands into the tub again. If their Mary Jane was offered that job in The Bible & Tract Depot, and she took in extra washing, she might even

11

be able to afford the lad a pair of shoes for his schooling! Then he wouldn't need to feel ashamed of being poor. That's what she'd do! She'd get him a pair of shoes!

Margaret Wilson had then called on Hannah Grigs. A tall, skinny, awkward girl of seventeen, who looked as though a good meal wouldn't do her any harm. This time, instead of sitting in a steamy kitchen with a pile of washing, she had been shown into a large gloomy room resembling a ships cabin. There were charts, maps, globes and memorabilia from all over the world. The only feminine touch came in the shape of two sisters who were surrounded by dresses, skirts, materials, bobbins and pins. Ruth Grigs's, Hannah's older sister and the dressmaker in the family, had been delighted at Margaret Wilson suggestion that Hannah be employed as shop girl by The Bible & Tract Depot. Hannah had a lively mind and since leaving school it had become increasingly obvious to Ruth, that her sister needed suitable employment. Now this kind offer from The Bible & Tract Depot, would at least give the girl a focus in life. Goodness knows, she had no sewing ability whatsoever! In fact every time Ruth had asked for her help you could guarantee the garment would have spots of blood where Hannah had pricked her finger or the stitches would be too large. She'd even been known to catch the article of clothing she was sewing, up with the pinafore she was wearing and Ruth had spent the best part of the evening unstitching both garments before stitching them back up again. Hannah really was so clumsy!

Margaret Wilson arrived back at The Bible & Tract Depot late afternoon and sank wearily down on the stool behind the counter. Waves of tiredness washed over her. It had been a busy day but surely she shouldn't be feeling quite as exhausted as this.

'The Committee have suggested that you might like to go to Leeds to visit a shop similar to The Bible & Tract Depot.' Ephraim Lister had his back to her. He was unpacking the boxes of books delivered from the boat that morning. 'It sounds like quite a good idea to me. What do you...... ' Ephraim Lister turned, aware of the silence behind him and was disturbed to see his colleagues very white face. Concerned he jumped to his feet. 'Miss Wilson are you ill?'

She wanted to say 'No! Don't fuss Mr Lister,' but she felt as if there was a tight band across her chest. She opened her mouth but no words came. The room seemed unsteady. The books and the shelves swayed. She reached a gloved hand out towards the counter to steady herself but her arm felt heavy. As if in a dream she watched Ephraim Lister move smartly in her direction before an almost welcome blanket of darkness descended upon her and she collapsed on to the floor.

******

'But Thomas, it's an absolute *dream*!' Kate Benson clapped her hands together in delight and Thomas raised his eyebrows in surprise.

'I wouldn't exactly call it a *dream*, Kate dear, but it certainly has potential.'

The old farmer listened to them in some amazement. The handsome young couple stood side by side in his farmyard surveying the old gypsy caravan. Most of the once brightly coloured paint had flaked away leaving the caravan down to its original wood. The chimney on the roof was hanging off, a window was smashed and a rag, which must at one time have been a curtain flapped noisily through the gap. A wheel was broken, so were two of the steps leading up to the door, which was hanging off its hinges and these two thought it had, what did they call it? Potential! Whatever that was!

Thomas waved his arm toward the caravan. 'Can't you just imagine a dozen or more of these Gospel Vans carrying the Word of God to the outlying farms and villages which have no churches or chapels Kate?'

'Oh yes Tom! Yes!'

'I shall call it "Victory". What do you think?'

'Yes I like that, Tom. What is it like inside?' Gingerly she made her way up the steps, carefully avoiding the broken planks and poked her head warily around the door. 'It needs a few repairs, a new stove and the rug on the floor is rather dirty.'

A few repairs! Rather dirty! With a great deal of effort the farmer contained a snort of mirth. This caravan was a load of old junk! If it hadn't been that his hens had taken a liking to it he'd have used it for firewood long ago.

'I'm planning for The Bible & Tract Depot to supply us with Bibles and books. I even wondered if one of our churches could employ a missionary to live in the caravan selling the books and preaching the Word of God. If the local farmers can supply us with horses then the whole

13

venture might not be too expensive.' Thomas followed Kate into the dingy caravan and the farmer shook his head in disbelief.

'Phew! Thomas, it smells!' Kate wrinkled her nose up in disgust. 'I shall supply packets of lavender to sweeten it up.'

Thomas looked at his cousin fondly. 'You really think it'll work Kate? I mean the missionary, the books, the travelling around and everything.?'

'Of course it will.' she affirmed gently. 'It's a brilliant idea. A God inspired idea!' On the spur of the moment, Thomas wrapped his hand around hers. It was small and warm to the touch and sent a thrill of excitement through him.

Thomas Bainbridge had known Kate Benson since they were children. Their fathers, John Benson and Emerson Muschamp Bainbridge had not only been good friends from their younger days but had become brothers-in-law when John married Emerson Muschamp's sister. Tom's relationship with Kate however, had always been one of playmate when they were children and total indifference when they were in their early teens. He had only become more aware of his attractive cousin during the past three years when she had developed into a beautiful young lady and moved out into society. During that period of awareness he discovered there were a number of things he respected about Kate. One of them was that she could be as enthusiastic as himself in new ventures and the other was her deep faith in God. This was something Thomas Bainbridge cared about deeply. If ever he was to marry it must be to someone like Kate Benson.

'Kate?' He squeezed her hand.

Yes? Oh Tom look. The hens have laid eggs on the bed here.' She pulled her hand away from his and kneeling on the dirty floor picked up three eggs. 'I shall take them out and give them to the farmer.'

Thomas sighed. The only problem with Kate Benson, was that she talked too much!

After a quick examination of the inside of the caravan, Thomas followed his cousin outside. The farmer was being presented with the three eggs as though the hens and their produce didn't belong to him anyway. He was nodding his head and thanking her most politely.

'Have you had a word with the local farmers about lending their horses to pull the caravan Farmer Dodds?'

'Yes sir, and as I predicted, most of them were delighted with the idea of a travelling church." He cleared his throat in an embarrassed manner. 'Would you and Miss Benson care to have tea with us sir. Mrs Dodds has some home made jam and freshly baked bread.'

Kate Benson's eyes lit up and she turned pleadingly to Thomas. 'We'd love to Mr Dodds, but I'd like to take a walk down by your river first though, if you have no objections that is?'

'None at all sir. Just call in at the farmhouse when you're hungry. The kettle will be on the hob.'

The skies had brightened up somewhat as the day had progressed and a thin watery sun was sending shimmering rays across the Coquet River as Thomas and Kate meandered along the riverbank. Kate pulled her scarf tightly around her neck. 'Are you sure you don't want to go fishing Thomas? I don't mind sitting in Mrs Dodds' kitchen till you've caught something.'

'You've got your eye on her freshly baked bread and home-made jam Kate Benson, that's why you don't want to go fishing with me.' Thomas teased.

Kate chuckled. "That's true." They walked in a comfortable silence for a while then she asked, 'How long have you been coming here Tom?'

'Mmm? About four years.'

Four years! How did you get to know Farmer and Mrs Dodds?'

Thomas smiled at the memory. 'I called and asked them if I could fish from their land and they were most obliging. Then one day I got caught in a thunderstorm. They not only dried me out and invited me to stay for a meal, but insisted on giving me a bed for the night, the weather being too atrocious for travelling. I soon became a regular visitor to their home and our discussions moved on to faith in God.' Thomas shrugged, slightly embarrassed. 'Before long, Mr Dodds and his good wife came to know our Lord.'

A look of admiration crossed Kate's face. 'What a lovely story Tom. Is that how you became involved in the outlying districts of Northumberland.?'

'Partly. Father and I have been leading cottage prayer meetings in the area for some time now. Hopefully one day they'll all have chapels, but..... but there was a matter I wanted to talk over with you Kate.'

'Ah yes. The Gospel Van. I do think...'

'No, we can talk about that later.'

Kate threw up her hands. 'I know! I know! I shouldn't have barged into The Bible & Tract Depot this morning when you had a meeting. Poor Miss Wilson is rushed off her feet anyway without me taking up more of her time.'

'No it's not The Bible & Tract Depot, Kate. I really want to....'

'Look Thomas! Oh look! A hawk! Isn't it beautiful?'

Kate tilted her head and watched the bird flying fast and low along the course of the river, the milky sun glistening on its broad slate-grey feathers. She shaded her eyes and for a few moments they watched the hawk rise slowly towards the grey leafless trees where the wind faintly whispered through empty branches. As it circled it watched the young couple warily.

'Kate?' Thomas spoke gently.'

'Yes Tom?'

'Would you do me a favour?'

She turned smiling and dropped her hand from her eyes. 'Yes Tom. Anything. Do you want me to make curtains for the gospel.....'

'No- no. Not yet anyway.'

'What then? Do you......'

'Will you shut up for five minutes so I can ask you if you would like to ..... to walk out with me?'

'But Thomas, we are out walking.'

'No Kate. I mean...I mean....'

The hawk continued circling. There was nothing to frighten it away. Only a young couple below standing staring at each other in silence, absorbed in their own private world. He could land nearby and catch that field mouse and they'd never notice. He circled lower, assessing the situation. The couple moved ever so slightly. The hawk rose, but they had only moved closer so their arms could entwine around each other. The hawk swooped suddenly on his prey, landing within feet of the young couple but not a word nor a movement did he spot from them. His talons outstretched for the kill, his beak at the ready, his wings flapped, there was a squeal from his prey, then silence as he soared from the brown earthy field towards the milky sun again. Just in time! As he circled over the trees and across the fields the couple moved apart and Thomas Bainbridge and Kate Benson's delighted laughter echoed after him.

March 1869

The Quayside market was alive with its usual Sunday morning activities. Stallholders selling china plates, household goods and second hand clothes competed loudly with each other for custom. Shoppers, shivering in the cold March breeze and drawn by a smell of roasting chestnuts warmed their hands by the grid of hot coals. Chattering housewives clustered around stalls selling fresh cockles and mussels. Children with their mouths wrapped around fluffy balls of candy floss peered wide-eyed at cages of white mice scrambling over each other. The more adventurous children surreptitiously pooled their menial pocket money to buy itching powder to make someone's life a misery. Steam boats and sailing vessels smelling of tar and wet canvas lined up along the Quayside loading or unloading their cargo, the sailors shouts mingling with the call of the traders.

Annie Stephenson loved the atmosphere of the Quayside, or "Paddy's Market" as it was called locally. Normally she would have been on her knees rummaging among the rows of second hand clothes laid out on the cobbles, but this morning she hardly gave them a glance. This morning she was returning from delivering the extra washing she'd taken in so she would have enough to buy her John a pair of second hand shoes for his school. She pulled her thin shawl tightly around her shoulders, her fingers clutching at the few coins she'd earned that morning. What with the bit extra their Mary Jane was making at The Bible & Tract Depot and the income from this morning, she might even be able to run to a pair of trousers for him as well.

The kitchen was empty when she arrived home. She breathed a sigh of relief. Flinging her shawl on the large wooden table she sank down in the chair beside the empty fire grate and slowly let her eyes wander around her kitchen. They didn't have much in the way of furniture and through the week the kitchen was always piled high with other people's washing but today, Sunday, was the one day she could call her kitchen her own again. Sunday was the day the wash tub and poss-stick were relegated to the corner. Perhaps if Lady Fortune had been kinder to Annie Stephenson she might even have been house proud but at least she could pride herself on being able to pay the rent on time. The rent money was stored in a hiding place Ted could never find!

Annie pulled off her shoes. They were worn and had a hole in the bottom letting in the wet but she couldn't afford a new pair, not yet at any rate. She wriggled her toes in front of the empty grate wondering where everyone was. She was surprised Ted was out. He'd had more than his usual skinful at the pub last night and she'd expected to hear him still snoring in bed.

She had no idea where John could be either. At least that was one good thing about him going to school, she'd know where he was and thanks to Mary Jane's new job, she was off the streets. No good could come of a fifteen year old girl spending her time on the streets!

She suddenly remembered the extra money she'd been given that morning. Best get that hidden away before his lordship arrived home. She rose from her chair and padding across the stone kitchen floor in her bare feet, carried her few precious coins to a dining chair in the corner. It was one of her bargains from Paddy's Market. The upholstery had at one time been shiny black hair cloth, supported by springs and horsehair padding but through age, strands of horse hair had escaped guaranteeing the bottom of the sitter would be severely pierced! That was why no-one ever sat on it and why it was Annie's private hiding place, separate from the rent money and special to her alone. Carefully she pushed the coins into a neat slit she'd made under the seat and heard a slight 'clink' as it joined the others she'd saved towards John's school shoes.

'I knew you'd have a place! I just knew it!'

Startled she turned to face her husband's large form filling the kitchen door, his face contorted with rage, his eyes still heavy and red from the previous night's drinking. She hadn't heard him come in but perhaps he'd been in the house all the time, asleep in the bedroom. She should have checked. She was stupid not to have checked.

'Don't touch that money Ted. Please don't. It's for our John's school shoes.'

'School? What's he want schooling for? He doesn't need schooling. Look at me! I never had any schooling!'

'Aye' Annie thought. 'Just look at y'self, y' big slob!' but keeping her voice deliberately calm said, 'Our John's really excited about getting a new pair of shoes for his schooling Ted. Let's not disappoint him.'

'And what happens if I need that money?'

Annie bit back a sharp retort about the needs of the rest of the family and stared defiantly at her husband. They'd been a handsome couple at one time, her and Ted, but losing three children had brought more than untold grief upon them. Although barely forty, both were prematurely grey, and Annie soon discovered Ted's way of handling his grief was to hit the bottle which soon affected his ability to work. Now her once fine figure of a man had a paunch, a red face and was frequently violent.

18

'Hand it over woman!'

She moved protectively in front of her chair. 'No Ted.' The firmness in her voice did little to betray the quaking going on inside her. 'We've given the boy precious little, you and me, we can at least buy him a pair of shoes so he can go to school with some sense of pride.'

'I know what I'll be giving 'im and I divint think it'll be shoes!' He lurched across the kitchen towards her still reeking of alcohol from the night before, still not fully out of its evil influence. Roughly he pushed her aside.

'No! No! Please Ted!' Regaining her balance she reached out a hand to pull him away from her chair but he shrugged her off.

'How do you get into this thing?' he growled tipping the chair on its legs.

She didn't say a word, she just stood wringing her hands anxiously. If he wanted the money he could damn well find out how to get it out of the chair himself!

'Pass that kitchen knife!'

She stood her ground. She would not lift one hand to help him get her money.

Reaching across her he grabbed the kitchen knife off the table and before she could stop him he'd slashed it across the black horsehair cover. Then picking up the chair, shook it till the precious hard earned coins tumbled out and rolled across the stone kitchen floor. She watched his eyes glistening, wild with greed as he eagerly stooped to retrieve them. With a deep sob of anguish she flung herself at him, flattening him back against the kitchen wall.

'I'll kill you for this Ted Stephenson! It's bad enough that you can't earn enough to feed us, but that you take every ....last .....farthing.... we.... have....' Her fists hammered on his chest, her fury fully aroused. For Annie, there was more to this money than a pair of shoes. Deep within her she was giving to John what she felt she had never given to the children she'd lost in the cholera epidemic. She was giving her son the chance they'd never had. A chance to live as a human being, away from the squalor and deprivation that had caused their deaths. Away from the ignorance and hopelessness she and Ted knew. Those coins represented a love Annie Stephenson had always been afraid to show her little boy in case he was taken away from her, like the others had been.

'Get off me woman! Get off!' Roughly he pushed her aside. He'd never seen her so worked up before. She came at him again but the influence of drink from the night before made his actions sluggish as he tried fending off her furious fists. He still held the kitchen knife in his hand, the one he'd used to slash her precious chair, but neither of them seemed aware of the danger it posed.

'Give over Annie! I need this money!' He gave her a hard shove and she tumbled backwards over the chair. Having a free hand Ted knelt back down to pick up the coins. Annie saw red. Snatching up the thick wooden stick she used for possing the clothes in her washing tub, she hurled herself at him with a loud cry. Ted glanced up just in time to see the stick and his enraged wife bearing down upon him. He tried standing up but she was upon him before he knew it so all he could do was lift his hands to protect himself.

Annie Stephenson didn't see the knife in his hand. Not that it would have made any difference anyway. She was a mother protecting the future of her son. In fact, so great was her fury that for a split second she didn't even feel pain as the blade entered her side. All she saw was the horrified expression crossing Ted's face. She stopped, uncertain, then slowly looked down at the kitchen knife and the red of her blood spreading across her clothes.

'Ted?' The anger seemed to be draining out of her and she felt a little strange. 'Ted?'

His face had turned grey. 'Oh God, Annie! What've I done!' His voice was barely a whisper. He staggered to his feet as he saw his wife swaying, but he was too slow to catch her. She crumpled in a heap, banging her head on the cast iron grate in the fireplace and lay very, very still. A red river of blood gushed from her temple and trickled over the grate into the ashes.

'Annie? Oh God Annie!' He stood looking at the crumpled, unconscious form of his wife with her deathly white face and he began to shake. 'It's your own bloody fault woman. All I wanted was the money for a...a.....' He couldn't say the word 'drink' because he couldn't contemplate the thought that drink had been so important to him that he'd even ...even....killed for it!

Blind panic, as bad as the time when he'd lost his three children suddenly set in. He wasn't thinking clearly or rationally. All he knew was that he had to get out! Quickly! Scrabbling around on his knees he snatched up the remaining coins, then thrusting them in his pocket fled out of the kitchen, almost knocking Mary Jane over at the front door.

'Where you going in such a rush da?'

Going? He didn't know where he was going! All he knew was that he had killed the only person who had been able to make any sense out of his life - and now he was doomed!

April 1869

Margaret Wilson had been working on the accounts for the past two hours but she looked up and smiled welcomingly as Ephraim Lister entered the small back room.

'Any luck Mr Lister?'

Ephraim sank down on the hard wooden chair opposite her with a sigh of relief.

'Yes, Miss Wilson. I think I may have found suitable accommodation for Mrs Lister and myself at long last - without stairs.' he added. He allowed himself a friendly smile at his depositary and was warmed by having it mirrored back. 'I must confess Miss Wilson, it will be a wrench to leave my role as supervisor of these premises. It won't be quite the same returning twice a week as secretary and book-keeper to a shop unknown to me. Yet in other ways I'm relieved. I think the travelling to and from London has made the work quite exhausting of late.' He surveyed the small cream walls of the office in which they sat, his eyes eventually landing back on his depositary. 'Yes,' he added softly, 'I shall miss this shop.'

A touch of sadness played around Margaret Wilson's mouth. 'I too will be sad to leave,' she said quietly.

Ephraim smiled at her. He understood as no-one else ever would, the hard work and dedication that had been needed in setting up The Bible & Tract Depot, and it was Margaret Wilson's part in that setting up that had forced her to resign.

Dr. Humble had announced that she was suffering from exhaustion when the Committee had asked the good doctor for his diagnosis of Miss Wilson's ailment. He had concluded that there was nothing seriously wrong with Miss Wilson but suggested that a little less work and a little more care and attention to her health would help.

Margaret Wilson played absently with the ink pot in front of her, being careful not to catch her fingers on the wet ink. 'It was the hardest letter I have ever written, my letter of resignation,' she said softly. "Oh don't misunderstand me,' she added hastily. 'I am more than grateful to Mr Richardson for asking me to teach my girls a few more hours a week. It will be a great help financially and there won't be the long hours.'

Then she spoke so quietly Ephraim almost had to lean forward to catch what she said. 'I'm sure the new premises acquired from Mr Pigg, the tailor are much more suitable and of course being just across the road makes it very convenient for transporting stock, but ....but somehow I've grown fond of this building.' She hesitated. 'We've made it into such an elegant shop - you and I.' She caught his eye and for a moment they were drawn together by memories of the first four years they had shared in establishing and building up of The Bible & Tract Depot. Then hastily she dropped her eyelids and her voice had its usual touch of efficiency about it when she said, 'I've brought the ledgers up to date so you shouldn't have any difficulty in following my figures Mr Lister, and when my replacement starts work I shall of course brief her.'

Ephraim Lister didn't reply. She raised her eyelids and found him looking at her with a hint of, could it be affection she saw in his eyes? He gave an embarrassed cough.

'I hope you will forgive my impertinence Miss Wilson, but I would like to say I . .er... I have found it a great pleasure, a very great pleasure working with such a dedicated person as yourself.'

A flush of embarrassment spread across Margaret Wilson's face but she was powerless to do anything about it. 'Thank you Mr Lister.' she murmured. 'I feel we have worked well as a team.'

'Indeed we have Miss Wilson. Indeed we have, and perhaps we have set this shop on the way to greater things?'

'Yes. Who knows.' she replied and they were comfortably silent for a long time, these two people who had given out so much in their work for The Bible & Tract Depot, at No. 55 Pilgrim Street. Eventually Ephraim asked, 'How was Mrs Stephenson when you visited her?'

She knew it was right that he had broken into their comfortable silence by changing the subject but in some ways she was sad that he had.

'Well she's alive, if you can call lying in bed staring at the walls all day, living! Dr. Humble says the will to live seems to have been drained out of her. Nobody seems to know the whereabouts of Ted Stephenson. Hiding

22

up somewhere no doubt.' She shook her head. 'All for the sake of poor John's shoe money. Poor child. It's as well we can offer Mary Jane extra hours to help us move because at the moment that is the only wage going in the house, until the mother is well enough to work again.'

'Has Mary Jane talked about the incident?'

'Not much. All we know is, she arrived home to find her mother lying unconscious in a pool of blood and the chair, where she had hidden the money, slashed by a knife. Apparently her father almost knocked her off her feet as he raced out of the house so it wasn't hard to come to a conclusion of what had taken place. The poor girl began screaming for help. Fortunately the good Dr Humble was in the area at the time. It's a bad business. Very bad.'

'Has the incident affected Mary Jane's work?'

'Only a little.' Margaret Wilson wiped a smattering of wet ink that had found its way on to her fingers, on to her handkerchief. 'She's a hard worker though. Packing, scrubbing and cleaning ready for the move and she certainly doesn't dawdle when she's running errands for us. I think we'd have been lost without her these past few weeks.'

'And her brother John starts school when?'

'I'm not sure. I gather there is some delay with regards to needing parent's signatures. But whenever he does start it will be without shoes.. Poor child.'

'Mm.' Ephraim thought of his own two boys, only a few years older than John. He'd never been on a high wage but they'd never been forced to go to school without shoes and warm clothing and he took pride in that.

'Please don't ask me how Hannah Grigs, the Baptist girl is doing.'

Ephraim raised his eyebrows. Margaret Wilson had a habit of calling her "the Baptist girl".

'Hannah is the clumsiest young woman I've ever met. No wonder her sister Ruth was so delighted when we offered her the post of shop girl. I only hope our new depositary is a tolerant person. Hannah's only saving grace is her pleasant disposition and genuine desire to help.'

Ephraim didn't reply. He was still thinking of John and his shoes.

******

Hannah Grigs carefully stepped down off the stepladder and with her head tilted to one side surveyed the empty shelves. 'The shop looks empty without books on its shelves, doesn't it Mary Jane?' There was a touch of sadness in her voice. 'It doesn't look like a book shop any more. It looks.....dead!'

Mary Jane snorted. It was a pretty name for a fifteen-year old girl who wasn't particularly pretty but then that could have something to do with her being undernourished and wearing ill-fitting, second hand clothes. She was a small girl with dark hair and striking black eyes that regarded everyone with suspicion. Except lately, since she had started work in The Bible & Tract Depot, they had softened considerably. Possibly because, like her brother John, she had found only kindness and acceptance in this place and knew that as long as she worked hard, she was guaranteed a fair wage for her labours.

She shovelled more coal on to the fire. 'You do talk daft at times Hannah Grigs. You really do!'

Undeterred, Hannah stared around the shop with its piles of neatly stacked books tied with string, waiting to be transferred to the new shop. Her mousy brown hair was tied back into a long plait and had wispy cobwebs clinging to it. The white smock covering her willowy figure was smudged with dirt. 'Removing everything like this is like taking the very life out of the shop.' she said sadly.

'Aye well, there'll more than the shop having the very life taken out of it if you divvint stop your dreaming! Do you want some of this hot water for scrubbing the shelves or not?'

Hannah sighed. 'The trouble with you Mary Jane Stephenson, is you have no romance in your soul." Reluctantly she picked up the duster and climbed unsteadily up the ladders again. 'Yes, pour some of that water into a bucket would you please?'

Mary Jane eyed the girl apprehensively. They'd only been working together for a short time but she'd already got the measure of her new friend. If ever there was anything to go wrong in The Bible & Tract Depot, you could guarantee Hannah Grigs was at the bottom of it and Hannah climbing up ladders didn't bode well in Mary Jane's eyes.

Despite the differences in their class and backgrounds the girls had developed a growing respect for each other. Mary Jane discovered that Hannah never looked down on her for being unable to read or write but kindly read the addresses on the parcels she had to deliver. She, in turn, quietly undertook to keep Hannah and her clumsiness out of trouble.

'Are you sure you know what you're doing? You divvint look too steady on them ladders. Will I do the scrubbing eh?'

'No, I'm fine. Anyway, Miss Wilson asked you to take the remaining coal over to the new shop.' Hannah wafted her duster across the top shelf and clouds of dust floated across the shop counter. 'Hurry up with that water Mary Jane, I can't stand at the top of these ladders all day.'

Mary Jane lifted the kettle from the fire and poured the hot water into a bucket. 'You'll have to come down a few steps so I can hand it up.' She staggered across the room with the bucket of steaming water and somehow the girls managed to transport it up the stepladder. Hannah set it down on the ledge at the top and thrust her hands vigorously into the water.

'Aahh! It's hot!' She jumped, splashing hot water over Mary Jane.

'Hoy! That was on my head!'

The girls giggled. They enjoyed these rare moment on their own. It had enabled their relationship to grow into a friendship. Unfortunately those times never lasted very long. Like now. The shop door opened and a smartly dressed woman with sharp aquiline features entered. She appeared to be in her early thirties. A neat straw hat with a navy ribbon around the brim, crowned fair hair tightly rolled into a bun. A cream summers dress with neat pleats and a high neck showed off a trim figure.

From her precarious position at the top of the ladder, Hannah turned. She was about to apologise for the mess and inform the customer that the shop was closed for the day due to moving premises, when the door opened again and the most attractive young man she had ever set eyes on entered. Her mouth fell open. He looked up at her, this tall, fair, young man and his wide generous mouth broke into a wide smile.

The woman's sharp, high pitched voice broke the spell. 'I am Miss Elisabeth Smith. I'm the new depositary and I'm here to see Mr Lister and Miss Wilson.'

'Mm' Hannah remained staring at the young man. He raised his eyebrows questioningly. She'd never had a young man take an interest in her before and she couldn't quite make up her mind whether she liked the way her heart was pounding and everything else had drifted into insignificance. Mary Jane watched the exchange from the corner of the shop with interest.

'Young girl! I *said*, I am Miss Elisabeth Smith. I am the new depositary and I'm here to see Mr Lister and Miss Wilson!' The woman moved to the bottom of the stepladder and tapped sharply on the side. She shouldn't have done that. Hannah was unsteady enough on the ladders without someone tapping on them. It was bound to unsteady the girl. Mary Jane could see what was going to happen but stood there, helpless.

Startled out of the wonderful process of falling in love, Hannah jumped, the ladder shook, she reached out to grab the shelves, tilting the ladder and the bucket slowly slid off the top ledge. Mary Jane watched with mingled delight and horror as very hot dirty water poured from a great height all over Miss Elisabeth Smith, their new depositary. The wet duster draped itself over the front of her straw hat and the bucket fell with a clatter at her feet. There was a cry of alarm from Hannah as she lost her footing.

The young man leapt forward and just as the ladders toppled over he caught her. 'Steady!' His accent was Scottish, and although he kept his arm around her as he brought her safely to the floor, his eyes were fixed anxiously on the new depositary, Miss Elisabeth Smith.

Her face, or what could be seen of it behind the wet duster, was a mask of fury. The front of the cream summer dress hung limp, wet and steaming. Mary Jane held her breath. Miss Elisabeth Smith slowly pulled the wet duster from the front of her straw hat and when she spoke, her voice was quivering with rage.

'I said, I am Miss Elisabeth Smith!' Her neat gloved hand dropped the wet duster on to the counter. 'I am the new depositary and I am here to see Mr Lister and Miss Wilson!' She glared at the young man with his arm still around the shop assistant's waist and turned her head slowly in Mary Jane's direction. 'You girl!' She pointed a sodden grey glove in her direction. 'Go and tell them I'm here!'

Mary Jane didn't hesitate. She fled up the stairs two at a time. There was no way she could get her friend out of this mess! She didn't even bother knocking when she reached the office but charged breathlessly into the room. Mr Lister and Miss Wilson looked up surprised.

'Have you forgotten how to knock on a door before you enter Miss Stephenson.' Mr Lister, even in a crisis was a stickler for etiquette. 'Now go out and come back in the correct way!'

'Please Sir, Miss...' Mary Jane turned appealingly to Miss Wilson.

'Out!'

Mary Jane scurried out. Her knees were shaking. There was going to be the most awful row. She waited a moment then gently knocked on the door.

'Come in.' Mr Lister didn't sound at all pleased.

'What is it Miss Stephenson?' Miss Wilson could see the girl was agitated.

'Please Miss, it's Hannah...er Miss Grigs. There's been a bit of....trouble.'

Margaret Wilson felt her heart sink. She was hoping her last few days were going to be quiet ones. 'Trouble? What sort of trouble?'

'Er....'

'Well girl? What has Miss Grigs been doing?'

'She's...she's...'

'Yes? Yes?'

Mary Jane Stephenson stood in the middle of the office and suddenly the whole episode downstairs struck her as being extremely funny. 'She's been ...been ......baptising the new depositary Miss!'

Mr Ephraim Lister and Miss Margaret Wilson exchanged horrified glances before rushing passed her out of the door. Mary Jane suddenly realised she was grinning. Then she began to give voice to a chuckle which seemed to grow from the very depths of her being. Within a few moments her infectious laughter was echoing around No 55, Pilgrim Street. It had been a long time since Mary Jane Stephenson had found anything to laugh about. She laughed as she hadn't laughed in a long, long time and with her laughter came the welcome release of the tensions placed upon her over the past few weeks.

June 1869

The locals said you could always expect wet weather at the end of June, when the Town Moor held the Annual Horse Race Meeting, but this year was an exception. The sun blazed down on the 1,000 acres of open greenery just north of the city centre, but then the sun had shone every day for Thomas Bainbridge, ever since Kate had agreed to become his sweetheart. Today, while she was having tea with friends, he decided a day at the Races, furthering his interests with the Temperance Movement, was a good way of occupying his thoughts.

The Temperance Movement, which was avidly supported by the Committee of The Bible & Tract Depot, advocated non-alcoholic beverages in an attempt to attract men away from the Race Meeting where there was much drinking and drunkenness. The activities of the Temperance Movement were still comparatively small, just a few children's games, competitions and speakers giving vent to their beliefs on the evils of alcohol. The Movement hoped and prayed that one day horse racing would be abolished from the Town Moor altogether and they could have a Temperance Festival in its place.

Crowds were already gathering around the track. pushing and vying for the best view. Children crawled through the legs of adults to take up a place at the front. Stallholders selling beer had no need to draw attention to their wares, for men crowded around, anxious to have a drink in their hand before the first race. Horses snorted impatiently in the ring, their ears twitching at every sound, their coats gleaming, their tails flicking at flies active in the hot June sun. There was a pungent smell of beer and horses.

'Thomas! Thomas!'

Thomas Bainbridge turned to see Mr William Stephens, the ship owner waving to him. He made his way across the grass, passed the tik-tak men taking bets, their arms waving wildly in the air, towards a small group of men talking by the Temperance Movement's podium with its banner over the top.

Mr Joseph Maher had brought some tracts from The Bible & Tract Depot and was arranging them on a small trestle table. They warned of the evils of alcohol but judging from the lack of interest, the crowds preferred the evil!

Mr John Alexander, a member of the British and Foreign Bible Society, Mr Thomas Pumphrey, the grocer and a few other affluent businessmen of the city smiled welcomingly as he approached.

'How is Miss Kate today Thomas?' Mr Alexander asked.

'Very well thank you Mr Alexander. She's having tea with friends.'

'Ah! Quite a delightful young lady. She will make someone an excellent wife one day. Don't you agree Mr Pumphrey?'

Mr Pumphrey's eyes twinkled. 'She will indeed. If I were a few years younger....'

For some inexplicable reason Thomas found himself blushing. It was one thing having Kate as a sweetheart - but a wife?

'How would you like to be one of our speakers this afternoon Thomas?'

No wonder their smiles had been welcoming! 'Who me?'

28

'Why not?' Mr Alexander smiled jovially at the young man. 'You usually have plenty to say on the sins of alcohol and you're experienced in preaching in the Methodist Church. Why not speak for us today?'

Thomas looked around at the crowds of people anxiously awaiting the forthcoming race. He couldn't handle this type of public speaking. It was one thing standing in a pulpit speaking to people who wanted to hear what you had to say but quite another matter making your opinions known before men, half of whom were drunk before the first race!

'Go on Thomas! You're a born speaker!' Words of encouragement filtered through his apprehension..

'Well I suppose.....' A moment later he found himself standing on the small podium.

He looked around. No one was looking in his direction. No one.

'Gentlemen! May I have your attention!' he began nervously.

A couple of women glanced curiously in his direction but as soon as they saw it was the Temperance Movement, lost interest and wandered away. A few curious children, bored with their games, stopped what they were doing to watch this new form of entertainment.

'I have news that could change your lives!' Thomas's voice carried nervously across the field. A couple of men stopped to listen. There was time to be amused before the race. 'I have a way of life for you that could make a difference!' A man with a tankard of beer in his hand turned towards the podium. Thomas Bainbridge's confidence began to grow as he became more accustomed to open air speaking. After all, hadn't the founder of his own Methodist Church, John Wesley, been an instrument for God by speaking in the open air? But were his words actually having an effect on anybody?

A man stood in the crowd. His clothes were dirty and he looked as though he hadn't shaved for weeks. He stopped to listen. Not that he was particularly interested in what the young man had to say but he felt safer in a crowd. No-one noticed you in a crowd, especially if you were close to children. People automatically let their eyes drop to the child. So he stood and listened.

'Drinking is evil!' Thomas Bainbridge's face burned under the hot June sun.

Drinking is evil? Aye. He knew all about that. Hadn't it been the drink that had lost him his job, his wife, his home and his kids. Aye. The drink was evil all right but what he wouldn't give for a pint of beer right now. He licked his lips. They were dry and his throat was parched with the heat of the day.

'It rots your soul and it rots your body!'

Aye, but you can't do without it! It deadens the memories of standing by helplessly watching the cholera take three of your children, of losing your job, of watching your wife fall dead at your feet with the knife you'd stuck in her. Aye! Drink was the very devil but you needed it! He jangled the two remaining coins left in his pocket. He could place a bet and hope to win or he could buy a beer. It never occurred to him to buy food. Why should it? He'd taken to stealing his food from some of the posh houses in Jesmond and was managing quite well. He hunched his shoulders, pulled down his cap and sidled towards the beer stall. He had to pass the stand where the young man was enthusiastically speaking on the evils of drink, so he picked up one of the tracts from The Bible & Tract Depot and pushed it in his pocket. Not that he knew what it was all about for he couldn't read, but it was free wasn't it and these days he picked up anything that was free. With only the tiniest stab of conscience, Ted Stephenson handed over the last of his son's shoe money to buy his drink.

******

He was scared to open his eyes because if he did that meant the day was about to start and John Stephenson wasn't sure whether he wanted that to happen. Today was the big day. Of course more and more children were going to school these days but it gave him a thrill of excitement to know he was now one of them.

He'd heard some of the men talking outside the pub about it becoming a law to go to school, but many of them disagreed with that idea. Who would stay at home to help busy mothers take care of the littluns if all the older kids went to school? His mam did agree with schooling though and only the other day she'd said he must always be very grateful to Mr Richardson for giving him this chance. 'Times were changing' she said, 'and it would only be them what were book learners what would get on in life.' He was only eight, going on nine, but already he knew he didn't want to be standing on street corners begging all his life. He'd been to Upper Pilgrim Street and seen the posh kids go off to school every day. Not that he counted the Lister boys' as posh. They were only a couple of years older than him but they always looked very smart when they came out of The Bible & Tract Depot, with their clean shirts, polished shoes and slates to write on. He had even seen Arthur, the boy nearest his own age, spit on his shoe to get rid of a nasty scuff mark where he'd fallen over a pile of books that soppy Hannah Grigs had left lying in the middle of the shop floor.

He would like to have proper clothes, proper schooling, a proper job when he grew up. He wriggled in his bed but still kept his eyes tightly shut. It was a sunny day. He knew that because he could feel the early morning sun streaming through the kitchen windows, warming the covers of his bed. Mary Jane had insisted he had a bath last night for his first day at school. He'd fought like the dickens with her but she'd hurled him in his mam's wash tub after she'd finished the washing and given him a good scrubbing with the brush. It had hurt like the blazes but he must have looked good because even his mam got out of bed to come and have a look at him. He was glad she was getting out of bed more. Mary Jane said she might even feel well enough to start work again soon.

The clip-clop hooves of old Patty as she pulled the milk cart up the street echoed through the open kitchen window. The Lister boys would probably have milk with their breakfast. He would be lucky if he got any breakfast! If he could read and write like the Lister boys, he'd be able to get a good job, then he'd be able to take care of his mam and Mary Jane and have milk for breakfast - but first he had to get to school.

His main concern was in case the boys at school poked fun at him about his face or about his ragged clothes and lack of shoes. That's what scared him most of all.

John Stephenson took a deep breath. If he wanted to learn to read and write so he could have milk in the mornings and a proper job, then he'd have to open his eyes and get out of bed and start the day. Anyway, Mary Jane would be barging into the kitchen in a minute to get breakfast so he better wake up.

John Stephenson forced an eyelid open. What he saw made the other shoot open in surprise. He sat up in bed with a jolt and stared at the items of clothing on the little stool beside his bed. Slowly he reached out and picked up the clean white shirt. He buried his face in it. It was slightly frayed around the collar and cuffs but it had that freshly laundered smell

31

about it. The grey trousers were a little bit thin around the knees but at least they didn't have holes in them and John Stephenson couldn't remember a time when his trousers hadn't had holes. There was a thick black woollen jumper with a few darns in the sleeves but it was as new as he'd ever worn. Slowly he slid his feet out of his bed and for a moment he could hardly breathe, for there in front of him was a pair of black polished shoes. Shaking with excitement he slid his feet into them. They fit! He bent down and ran his fingers over the toes. They were exactly like the ones Alfred Lister wore. Admittedly one of them had a nasty scuff mark where someone had fallen over something and scratched them, but for John Stephenson, they were the best, most perfect present he had ever had in the entire eight and a half years of his life!

17 Pilgrim Street
July 1869

The new premises of The Bible &Tract Depot at No.17 Pilgrim Street, stood squashed between two taller buildings each boasting an extra storey. Its bay window bulged out into the street but not far enough to attract the attention of passers-by. There were jewellery shops up and down Pilgrim Street and baker's shops with their warm bread and fancy cakes, and there was the affluent and fashionable Northumberland Street, just further up the road.

The Committee were alarmed to discover their new premises were in worse condition than they'd been led to believe. A source of heat coming from a closet was traced to a heating stove underneath their neighbours premises, so the adjoining wall had to be lined. Then the back yard flooded every time it rained because the flagging had sunk. Ephraim Lister ordered a small sink to be installed to carry off the standing water but it didn't seem to make an awful lot of difference.

Mr Ronald Watson, a builder, was employed to carry out this work but he'd hardly started before he was called away by Miss Wilson to sort out a chimney belching out smoke. On examination, Mr Ronald Watson discovered that the chimney stack was in need of urgent repair.

'Which do you want doing first?' he asked Mr Lister. 'The hot wall, the rotten woodwork, the smashed windows, the flagging in the yard or the chimney stack?'

Mr Ronald Watson was requested to start in the two rooms which were urgently required by the new depositary, Miss Elisabeth Smith, as living quarters.

'Before the Corporation pull down our old premises to make way for the new Police Station, Court and Fire Station, we're asking the Property Surveyor for the kitchen range from my old living quarters.' Empraim hastily explained. He and Miss Wilson were taking Miss Smith on a tour of inspection while the Committee, their friends and the staff, celebrated the opening of the new Bible & Tract Depot in one of the large rooms. 'Of course you will be supplied with paper and paint to decorate your living quarters,' he added.

Miss Elisabeth Smith's heart sank as she examined the dingy first floor living room and kitchen. Piles of soot lay on the hearth, the windows were broken and the walls dirty. How had she got herself into this situation? Here she was, living in premises that sorely needed attention and being paid by a firm that was barely holding its own financially. If it floundered, then so did she. This wasn't what she had expected at all when she'd been asked to take over Miss Wilson's post! Miss Smith was very conscious of her poor financial standing since the death of her father and she had thought to save money and travelling expenses by taking the two rooms offered her by the Committee. They had pointed out that as Mr Lister was no longer liviing on the premises, they needed someone who would be available to lock up after the various groups who rented their meeting rooms in the evening. It had seemed like a good idea at the time.

She followed her colleagues through into what would be her bedroom. It was very small. She walked over to the window. It was such a long way down to collect coal for her fire - all supposing they mended the chimney so she could have a fire!

Elisabeth Smith struggled to find a more positive note. Two and sixpence a week was, after all, a very reasonable rent and there was a lovely view across the town. She could just make out the horse drawn trams plodding up Pilgrim Street and around the corner into Market Street. She squared her shoulders. She really had no option and perhaps, just perhaps, she could be influential in making sure this place didn't flounder!. Bravely she turned to face her colleagues.

'I think these rooms will be very suitable, when they have been decorated.'

Miss Wilson smiled understandingly. 'Yes I think they will too. We shall ask Mr Watson to start repairing the chimney and windows straight away.' Sensitively she changed the subject. 'Should we join the others for tea, Mr Lister? Miss Smith?'

The one good thing about the new premises at No. 17 Pilgrim Street, was the large room on the first floor adjoining Miss Smith's living quarters. Today the tea party was being held in it but the Committee hoped it would be in great demand for renting. Enquiries had already been made from the Women's Temperance Movement and also the Young Men's Christian Association, the latter of which Mr Thomas Bainbridge was an ardent supporter. However, before this room could be rented out, it needed repairing, decorating and thoroughly cleaning. The cost of which only added to Mr Maher's worries.

As Mr Lister and his female colleagues made their way across the narrow unlit landing, they were greeted by Mary Jane Stephenson, clattering her coal scuttle up the stairs from the coal house in the back yard. Her white apron, donned especially for the occasion, was streaked with coal, her hair was awry from the wind outside and her face red from the exertion of climbing up the stairs. Elisabeth Smith frowned disapprovingly, Margaret Wilson shook her head in despair and Mr Ephraim Lister, sighed and opened the door for his errand girl. She staggered into the room with her bucket of coal and dragged it over to the fireplace.

It was a very grand tea party with sandwiches, scones, fancy cakes and home made biscuits. Mary Jane hadn't seen so much food in her whole life. Hannah Grigs was standing over by the fireplace pouring tea for members of the Committee, their wives and friends.

'After you have stoked the fire you may clean yourself up and join us Miss Stephenson.' Miss Wilson spoke quietly but the young girls delighted reaction was enough to make Henry Richardson's wife Anna, turn her head and smile. 'She's a sweet little thing, the errand girl.' she whispered to her husband. 'Isn't she John Stephenson's sister?'

'Mm?'

'Henry dear, I wish you would listen when I'm talking to you.' she chided gently.

'I was! I was! John Stephenson you said. He's a bright lad, quick mind. He'll be reading and writing in no time.'

Anna Richardson shook her head. Henry really was the limit. He was

34

getting older, deafer and was less alert than he used to be. He ought to be spending more time at home relaxing instead of with his boys in the 'Ragged School' or at his various committees. She'd even caught him helping Miss Wilson serve customers in The Bible and Tract Depot the other day.

'But I enjoy it dear.'he'd patiently explained.

She sipped her tea.

'Aren't they being evicted?'

'Who, Henry dear?'

'His mother and sister. The Stephensons.'

'Are they? Goodness me!' Anna Richardson placed her cup back in its saucer. 'Have you heard of this sorry state of affairs Miss Benson?'

Kate Benson moved over to join Henry and Anna Richardson. She wore a pretty pale lilac dress, edged in brown and pinched neatly in at the waist. A petite lilac hat with a brown feather perched elegantly on top of her head. 'What sorry state of affairs would that be Mrs Richardson?.'

'The errand girl's family are being evicted.'

'Oh goodness!' There was genuine distress in Kate Benson's voice. 'What will the family do? Tom dear, did you know about this?'

Thomas Bainbridge was reluctantly drawn into the conversation. He would much rather have continued exploring his interest in farming with Mr Angus. 'What are we talking about?' he asked.

'The errand girl's family is being evicted my love. Is there nothing you can do to help them?'

'I think I have my hands pretty full with the Bainbridge business, church work and setting up this Gospel Van my dear, don't you?" He instantly regretted his comments when he saw the tell-tale pursed lips. "What can I do?' he added shrugging his shoulders.

Anna Richardson turned to her husband. 'Didn't I hear you say the Committee needed a cleaning woman Henry?'

'Did you? I mean did I?' Henry Richardson frowned thoughtfully. 'I can't remember saying......'

'But of course whoever took the post would have to be willing to take the two rooms in the attic as well.'

Kate Benson caught the older woman's eye. 'What a brilliant idea Mr Richardson. Why I'm sure Mrs Stephenson would be ideal. Don't you think so Tom?'

'She probably would.' Thomas agreed, helping himself to another piece of cake, 'But.....'

'I knew you would agree Thomas.' Kate rested her hand affectionately on his arm.

'*But* the idea would need to go before the Committee.' he added.

'Well they're all here, you could ask them.'

'Kate dear, this is a tea-party to celebrate the opening of the shop, hardly a fitting time to....'

'But Thomas, an urgent thing like ...ah - Mr Maher.' Kate side-stepped into the elderly gentleman's path as he made his way towards the plate of ham sandwiches. 'Just the man we need to see.'

Joseph Maher eyed the remaining sandwich on the plate with a pang of regret before focusing his attention on the delectable Miss Benson. 'Yes my dear. What can I do for you?'

She beamed at the little man and his eyes twinkled in response. 'Tom and Mr Richardson have just been telling us The Bible & Tract are in urgent need of a cleaner and Mr Richardson has suggested the ideal person!'

'Oh? Who do you have in mind Henry?'

Henry Richardson opened his mouth but the words came from Miss Kate Benson. 'Mrs Stephenson. The errand girls mother.'

'Mm. But wasn't there a story of some family violence leaving her incapable of work?'

Kate waved her hand dismissively in the air. 'That was earlier this year. She's much better now.'

'Kate, we can't just accept her without going through the proper procedures.' Thomas objected.

Anna Richardson turned a winning smile on Thomas Bainbridge. 'I agree Thomas. In the normal course of things. But don't you think Henry's suggestion of Mrs Stephenson is most fortuitous, especially as the family are to be evicted.'

'Are they?' Joseph Maher's eyebrows shot up in surprise. 'Then it does appear we can not only solve their problem, but theirs. I shall have a word with Mr Alexander and Mr Pumphrey and er....yes, I'll get back to you.' He looked distastefully around the grimy walls of this large room. 'The sooner she can start cleaning this place up ready for renting the better.' His eyes rested back upon his four companions. 'Good work Henry,' he said patting Henry Richardson's shoulder. 'Excellent suggestion!'

Thomas Bainbridge, scratched his head in confusion before excusing himself to continue his fascinating discussion on farming with Mr Angus. Mr Joseph Maher hurried off to claim the last sandwich on the plate and after exchanging amused conspiratorial glances, Mrs Anna Richardson and Miss Kate Benson turned to converse with other members of the party, leaving Henry Richardson with a bemused furrow across his brow.

******

'Eee, our Mary Jane! I never thought I'd see the day we'd live in a posh place...like...this!' Annie Stephenson panted. She, Mary Jane and John were pushing a big wheelbarrow carrying their few meagre belongings up the steep cobbled hill from Lower Pilgrim Street, to Upper Pilgrim Street.

Mary Jane wiped her brow but kept pushing. 'Aye, well as long as you're up to doing the cleaning work ma. I'll help when I can but I'm kept pretty busy with deliveries.'

'I'll manage pet, divvint fret.'

'Our John, you'll have to sleep in the kitchen cos there's only two rooms.'

'Aye.' John's face was red with the exertion of pushing but he didn't mind. Moving to The Bible & Tract Depot premises was beyond his wildest dreams. He didn't care where he slept. Just being among all those books was enough for him.

'And you'll have to take over Alfred Lister's job of attending the door for the evening meetings in the big room.'

'Aye.'

'And you'll have to help me carry coal up to our room in the attic.'

'Aye.'

The wheelbarrow came to a halt outside the Bible & Tract Depot and the Stephenson family looked up at their new home.

A deep depression had fallen upon Annie Stephenson after Ted had run out on her. They had been through so much together, she and him, and despite all that had happened she missed him. Her physical recovery had been slow due to being undernourished. In fact if it hadn't been for Miss Wilson and some of her Quaker friends she would never have recovered. Gradually she had come out of her malaise, but not before the landlord had given them final notice for not paying their rent. She wasn't a praying woman, never had been. She'd prayed once, when her three children were dying of the cholera but it hadn't worked. She reckoned God had been too busy listening to the rich folk who went to church every Sunday to take any notice of what Annie Stephenson had to say. She prayed the night they were going to be evicted though and that had worked! That nice Miss Wilson had called the following day to say The Bible & Tract Depot needed her. Needed *her*? From a place of total despair, poverty and near starvation she was offered a home and employment by The Bible & Tract Depot, and it was a long time since Annie Stephenson had been offered anything.

'Aye, I'll keep this place as clean as a new pin,' she said quietly staring up at their new home.

Miss Elisabeth Smith stood behind the counter watching the arrival of her new neighbours. A poor, scruffy-looking bunch, perhaps, but they came highly recommended by Miss Wilson and Mr Lister, so she couldn't very well object. But they had better pull their weight! There was work to be done in this shop!

She watched her predecessor, Miss Margaret Wilson go with mixed feelings.

'If you have any queries, don't forget Mr Lister will be calling in twice a week to keep the books up-to-date and his successor, Mr William Smythe will be starting work tomorrow.' Margaret Wilson's gaze wandered around the new shop and tears welled up into her eyes. 'The books are the same but the shop.......?' She'd turned and her voice was shaking when she said, 'May God bless you for your work for this place Miss Smith.'

Elisabeth Smith, not used to emotional scenes just nodded, but as Miss Margaret Wilson walked out of The Bible & Tract Depot for the last time she heard a very quiet but determined, 'He will!' from behind the counter.

******

There was a clatter as Hannah Grigs, flushed from running, almost fell through the shop doorway. Miss Smith glared at her disapprovingly. She'd never really taken to either her or Mary Jane, since she'd been forced to discipline them over the water episode. 'And what is your excuse for being late this morning Miss Grigs?'

Sheepishly, Hannah hung up her coat. 'My apologies Miss Smith. My sister Ruth is making curtains for Miss Benson.'

Elisabeth Smith raised her eyebrows and the sarcasm wasn't lost on Hannah. 'So your sister making curtains for Miss Benson makes *you* late for work Miss Grigs? I don't quite see the connection. No! Don't try to explain!' She raised a warning hand to prevent the forthcoming garbled explanation. 'There is too much work to be done!'

There was a clatter, followed by a steady hammering from the basement where Mr Ronald Watson and his apprentice were starting work on lining the party wall.

Miss Smith gritted her teeth and looked at the stacked books waiting to be shelved.

'Right Miss Grigs,' she said sharply adjusting her spectacles. 'You can begin by displaying the Sunday School material over in that corner. Then perhaps you could stack the Scottish bibles in the shelves over by the window. After that I want you to get rid of those old magazines and the tracts damaged in the move. Burn them or something. The new colporteur will be calling in later this morning to choose his books. If he needs me, I will be in the basement. I have to see Mr Watson about the gas chandelier in the secretary's office. It's consuming too much gas and exhausting the air in the room.' She frowned at her shop girl. 'And do try to keep reasonably clean while you're busy. Remember you still have customers calling Miss Grigs.'

'Yes Miss Smith.' Hannah answered demurely and breathed a sigh of relief when she swept down to the basement to plague the life out of Mr Ronald Watson and his apprentice.

'What's a colporteur?' Mary Jane asked when she was safely out of the way.

'They're people who travel around selling Christian books.' Hannah's eyes gleamed excitedly for the new colporteur was Ian Clarkson, the handsome young man she had encountered during the unfortunate baptism of Miss Smith. He was from the Edinburgh Colporteur Society and had been engaged to work on the east side of the Newcastle district, and instructed to draw his books from The Bible & Tract Depot.

It was amazing how many customers came and went throughout the morning. Hannah was kept busy, but not too busy to keep her eyes open for Ian Clarkson. When he arrived he was pleasant and friendly but spent the majority of the time choosing his books. By mid-day, Mary Jane had lit the fire in the shop and swept the floor for the steady trail of Ministers, Sunday School teachers, scholars and browsers crossing their threshold to examine the new premises. None of them appeared to be in the slightest way distracted by the loud hammering from the basement. Of course the pleasant atmosphere was also helped by the absence of Miss Smith, who was otherwise occupied instructing the fitting of a small gas stove in the basement. Mary Jane had watched its arrival with relief. Now they had somewhere to heat the kettle in the summer instead of lighting the fire.

The shop was exceptionally warm that morning as Hannah was burning old magazines, tracts and rubbish they'd accumulated during the move. Too hot for a warm summer's day like today.

'Do you like working among books?' Ian shed his jacket and turned to Hannah who, was kneeling by the fire sorting Christian magazines. The majority of them were going to Captain Harrison, a friend of her fathers, for the use of his seamen. The remainder she was burning.

'Oh yes! I love reading, don't you?' She looked up at him and her eyelashes flickered coyly.

Mary Jane listened to their conversation on books with some degree of envy. . She could read a few words like "Pilgrim", for "Pilgrim Street" and "Pilgrim's Progress", and she knew how to write the first few letters of her name, but she would have loved to be able to read and write like Hannah and her young man. Not that he was her young man, at least not yet. They hadn't gone as far as walking out together but their liking for each other was patently obvious. Mary Jane sighed. It must be nice to feel attractive to someone. The image of Mr Ronald Watson's apprentice, Samuel sprang into her mind. He'd had the nerve to whistle at her this morning when he'd come into the shop. Cheeky thing! She wondered if he had found her attractive. Mary Jane smiled to herself. Perhaps, as soon as she'd finished wrapping this book for delivery she'd comb her hair, wash her face and tidy herself up a bit. Couldn't do no harm.

'Here's a few more magazines for burning,' she said handing Hannah a pile of crumpled paper.

Distractedly Hannah took them from her. Her face was red from the heat of the fire.

'Have you read any of the works published by the Christian Knowledge Society?' she asked crumpling the magazine.

'One or two.' he answered.

Her gaze never left Ian, who was absorbed in choosing books from the shelves in front of him. Abstractly she threw the paper on the fire.

Ian Clarkson picked a book from one of the shelves. 'I thought this one might be quite useful or...this one..'

A startled cry of alarm from Mary Jane, made him turn sharply. The carelessly thrown magazine had rolled from the fire on to Hannah's lap. In an instant the flame had caught her dress. She leapt up screaming, flapping her burning dress with her hands. Mary Jane stood frozen with fear but in three long strides, Ian Clarkson had crossed the room and was beating out the flames with his bare hands. Flaming pieces of paper floated across the room, lighting the old, dry magazines in the corner.

'The...the...' Numbly Mary Jane pointed to the corner.

'Oh my goodness!' Suddenly Miss Smith was darting across the shop floor. 'Water!' she shouted at Mary Jane. 'Get water!'

At the sharp directive, Mary Jane sprang into action. Turning on her heel she raced out to the back yard, her heart pounding with fear. Grabbing the heavy bucket of rain water she staggered back inside the shop with it. Hannah was crying hysterically. Ian was wrapping his jacket around her smouldering skirt and Miss Smith was struggling to stamp out the flames which were gaining momentum on the old magazines in the corner. Mary Jane didn't hesitate. She aimed her bucket of water at the magazines and threw! It would have been all right if Miss Smith hadn't manoeuvred herself between the burning magazines and the oncoming water. There was a gasp from the good lady, which was quite understandable with flames licking her skirt from behind and cold water dowsing her from the front! In fact if it hadn't been for the arrival of Samuel, Mr Ronald Watson's apprentice, whose quick thinking in throwing a mat over the magazines to suffocate the flames, there is every likelihood the Bible & Tract Depot would be needing for other premises!

'Oh my.....!' An astonished Ronald Watson stood by the basement door surveying the sorry scene before him. The usually immaculate Miss Smith's clothes were dripping and smouldering. The deluge of water had knocked her hair out of its fashionable bun and it hung limp across her shoulders. Her glasses were lopsided across her white frightened face and her whole body was shaking. Ronald Watson didn't usually feel sorry for folk, but at that moment he felt very sorry for Miss Elisabeth Smith.

The young shop girl, Hannah Grigs sat shaking on the floor. Her skirt was burnt and the colporteur was wrapping his handkerchief around her burnt hand. The errand girl, Mary Jane had shrunk back into a corner. Ronald Watson looked to Samuel for an explanation as the staff of the

41

Bible & Tract Depot were obviously incapable of speech.

'A fire.' the lad said simply.

'I can see that y' daft .....! Here, let's get these ladies seen to. You lass. Can you take care of the shop?'

Mary Jane's eyes opened wide. Take care of the shop? She'd almost burnt the place down! But all she did was nod her head while the workmen helped a distraught Miss Smith to her rooms and Ian took Hannah to the basement.

As soon as they'd gone Mary Jane forced her still shaking body into action. She swept up the charred magazines, washed the floor, tidied the hearth and then, as she'd promised herself, she washed her hands and face with what remained of the rainwater in the bucket and combed her hair. It was only as she sat down on the small stool beside the fireplace that she realised her hands were still shaking.

'Are you all right?' Samuel came back into the shop. He was a stocky young man with carrot coloured hair and freckles. His sleeves were rolled to the elbows and black braces held up trousers that appeared a size and half too big for him, but it was the genuine concern on his face that sent tears spilling down Mary Jane's cheeks.

'Come on, don't take on so.' He came over to the fireplace and pulling an old rag out of his pocket, handed it to her. 'Are you hurt?'

She shook her head and even more tears spilled down her face. She hoped a customer didn't come in. It wouldn't do to be behaving like this. 'It's just....just.....' All Mary Jane needed was someone to listen to her and Samuel Middlemass, the builders apprentice did just that, while The Bible & Tract Depot kept its doors firmly shut to give her that chance. Between sobs, it all came pouring out. The stabbing of her mother, fears of her violent father returning, the eviction and her deep sense of failure at not having been able to pay the rent. All the responsibility that had fallen on her young shoulders was now shed, between sobs, to this almost total stranger.

When she'd finished there was a comfortable silence between them. Then gently he took her hand. She noticed his were dirty from labouring in the basement and his fingernails were bitten, but she didn't mind. She glanced up at him from between her dark eyelashes and saw he was still watching her with that deep look of concern. A wave of self-consciousness ran through her. What was she thinking of, talking to a total stranger like this?

Then suddenly. almost as though he'd read her mind, his wide cheeky grin was back and his eyes crinkled in the corners.

'I like you Mary Jane Stephenson.' he said softly. 'I think you're...you're very brave. Do you fancy coming for a walk up Northumberland Street with me after work to look in the shop windows?'

Mary Jane suddenly felt like laughing, loudly and happily. So she did!

******

Elisabeth Smith thought she would never sleep that night, what with the shock of the fire and a strange new house to sleep in, but she was wrong. She woke only briefly through the night because she thought she heard someone creeping around but then she remembered that she had neighbours living above her and it was probably them that she could hear.

The following morning she was in the shop bright and early and feeling remarkably well despite yesterday's ordeal and was surprised to find Annie Stephenson already at work.

'Good morning Mrs Stephenson.'

'G'morning Miss.'

Elisabeth's eyes swept around the shop floor, landing on the table by the window. She frowned. 'Mrs Stephenson, have you removed the tablecloth from that table?'

'No ma-am. I just swept the floor and polished the counter.'

'Mm. Miss Grigs must have forgotten to put it on the table. I better unlock the door for her arrival, although no-doubt she'll be late again!' She lifted the keys from the hook by the door, but even before her fingers pushed the key into the lock she saw the jagged edges of the door frame. She froze.

'Mrs Stephenson,' Her voice was barely above a whisper. 'I think we've had intruders.'

As far as Ephraim Lister could make out, when he called later that day to introduce his successor, Mr William Smythe, to The Bible & Tract Depot, nothing had been taken except a tablecloth. Admittedly the premises were awash with builders, cleaners and removal men delivering further items of furniture for Miss Smith's apartment so it was rather difficult to say. Mr Lister and Mr William Smythe informed the police, calmed Miss Smith down and did whatever was necessary to set the shop in order again. Not a good start for No.17, Pilgrim Street or Mr William Smythe, Ephraim Lister decided as he left the shop later that morning. In fact today was not a good day to be working in The Bible & Tract Depot at all! Perhaps he'd be better off working on the books tomorrow. Perhaps!

******

The principal object of The Bible & Tract Depot was the sale of bibles of all description; pictorial and family bibles, gilt-edged, Scottish and other versions. They also sold periodicals, psalms, prayer books, hymn books, theological and books of a good moral standing and tracts were readily available for every outreach venture. Recently however, due to an increased demand from the Sunday School Union, the Committee had decided to explore having a stationery side to the business.

Mr Joseph Maher, the treasurer, was sitting in the office checking Mr Ephraim Lister's book-keeping figures. It had been decided a few years ago that after accumulation of net capital, that any surplus money be divided between the British and Foreign Bible Society, Newcastle Colportage Society and the Sunday School Union, but what with expanding the stationery side of the business, extra fire insurance, increased wages for the staff and the repairs Mr Ronald Watson was doing to the premises, their three beneficiaries, wouldn't be receiving very much this year! In fact, if it hadn't been for the amazing generosity of Mr Angus, one of their Committee members, who advanced a goodly sum on behalf of his Company, the Committee would never have been able to put in new windows to improve the shop. But money aside, and Mr Joseph Maher didn't often put the monetary worries of The Bible & Tract Depot to one side, after the disastrous start in No. 17 Pilgrim Street, matters were improving.. Mr William Smythe, was a responsible, middle-aged family man who appeared to be settling into the job very well. Sales had increased in the book department and since Mrs Stephenson had got to work cleaning the Committee Room, he'd even managed to persuade his wife to hire it for her Ladies Drawing Class every ·Thursday morning.

Joseph Maher closed the accounts book, removed his spectacles and rubbed his eyes. The gas lighting in this room was dreadful. Perhaps it would be worth considering closing the shop half an hour earlier during the winter months. Long exposure to these gas lights could cause injury to the books and it certainly wouldn't do the health of the staff any good either.

He stood up and wandered over to the window. It was a miserable September morning with a slow steady drizzle which hadn't eased up all morning. Horse drawn buses plodding wearily up Pilgrim Street, made detours around the rubble which had once been their premises. Curious barefooted children, oblivious to the weather, gathered on the corner of Market Street, watching the antics of a monkey on a barrel organ and a couple of well dressed ladies with their skirts lifted, crossed the puddles on the cobbled road. Mr Maher's eyes drifted towards a rather scruffy individual standing in a shop doorway opposite, staring into their shop. A tall, shifty looking character with a paunch and a red face, or at least what could be seen of it beneath his cloth cap. Mr Maher wasn't usually of a suspicious nature, but the recent break-in and missing tablecloth had alarmed them all.

The man must have sensed he was being watched. His wild, hunted eyes, scanned the windows, moving to the upper storey where Mr Joseph Maher's short, stocky figure stood silently watching him. Their eyes locked, momentarily, then abruptly the man hunched his shoulders and thrusting his hands into his pockets shuffled guiltily away.

Every day he'd stood across the road from The Bible and Tract Depot waiting to see his Annie. Every day since he'd chanced a sneak visit back to his home in Lower Pilgrim Street to find out about his children.

'They've moved.' he had been informed sharply by the new occupant, a large buxom woman smelling of ale, standing defensively by his old front door with her arms folded.

'Moved? Where to?'

The woman had shrugged. 'Last I saw of them, the mother and both kids were pushing their stuff up Pilgrim Street.'

'The *mother*?'

'Aye. Sickly woman.' Her eyes softened a little when she saw the colour drain out of his face. 'You could try that book shop on Upper Pilgrim Street where the daughter works. I hear tell they took the mother on as a cleaner.'

Ted had been stunned! After a wave of relief that his Annie was still alive and he wasn't wanted for murder, he was thrown into an overwhelming sense of guilt over what he'd done to his family.

Ted Stephenson had spent the past six months sheltering on a barge down by the Quayside and drinking himself into oblivion until his money ran out and he was forced to steal more. He'd even tried breaking into The Bible & Tract Depot where his Annie and children lived but an unexpected pang of conscience had come over him so he had just stolen the wool tablecloth for warmth had then left. He reckoned that he'd be better off down by the Quayside on a Sunday morning picking pockets.

The following Sunday morning, he had idly sauntered over to one of the soap boxes.

The local band of the Salvation Army with their dull red tunics and sparkling brass instruments were playing rousing tunes setting many a foot tapping. The women wore big bows on their bonnets and shook their tambourines with gusto in time to the music. There was quite a crowd of people listening to them and some of them threw pennies into a big drum. Ted looked around, assessing the crowd for possible pick-pocketing. The band finished playing and a young man stood up on the podium to speak. Ted's attention wandered until a familiar sentence rang a chord with him.

'Drinking is evil!' The young man spoke passionately.

'Aye,' Ted thought. 'I've heard that before.' Like most people, rich and poor, he knew the difference between good and evil and the meagre religious instruction in his life told him if the evil drink kept its power over him, he was in grave danger of the fires of hell.

'I have good news that could change your lives and get rid of the evil drink!' Ted Stephenson suddenly realised where he'd heard that message before. At the Races!

He pushed his hands into his pockets and his fingers curled around the small tract he'd picked up that day. He pulled it out of his pocket and stared blankly at the words in front of him.

'Do you want me to read it to you?' Ted jumped. An elderly man in a Salvation Army uniform stood in front of him with his hand held out for the tract. The cuffs were frayed on his jacket and his moustache was in need of a trim but there was no sense of fear as he addressed the shifty alcoholic in front of him. Wordlessly Ted handed the man his tract.

He'd never been a religious man but the tract talked about God being willing to forgive you for *all* your wicked ways if you confessed them to Him. It also said, if you were under the influence of the evil drink, He was well able to deliver you from it. The tract gave a message of hope and it had been such a long, long time since there'd been even a glimmer of hope

46

in his life that Ted Stephenson decided to listn.

The man finished reading and then looking Ted Stephenson straight in the eye asked him if he'd like to come to the Mission Hall. He'd be made welcome, there'd be someone he could talk to if he had a problem and he'd even get a meal.

Perhaps it was the meal or having someone to talk to, or perhaps it was because he had reached the bottom of the pit that Ted Stephenson felt the need to respond. Whatever the reason, he knew his life would have to change if there was to be any chance of getting Annie and his children back again. So that morning he found himself back at the Mission Hall talking about his drink problem to the man with the frayed cuffs. As far as he was concerned this was a new beginning and he wanted more than anything to tell Annie about his decision to change his way of life. So regularly, regardless of the weather, Ted Stephenson stood across the road from the shop trying to pluck up courage to approach his Annie.

******

The countryside along the Coquet River was always lovely at this time of year. The river rippled and sparkled under the milky sun as it wound its way down to the sea. Autumn leaves of yellow, brown, red and tired green clung to their branches until an early frost or gusts of wind made them a colourful carpet underfoot instead.

Thomas Bainbridge and Kate Benson crunched their way through the leaves as they made their way back to Mr and Mrs Dodds' farmhouse for tea.

'You're quiet Kate. Is there anything on your mind?'

Kate Benson hesitated. 'Just thoughtful Tom, that's all.'

'Do you want to talk about them?'

There was a moments hesitation. 'Not really.' she said quietly.

'I haven't upset you Kate dear, have I?' Thomas squeezed her hand affectionately.

Kate wasn't usually moody and that she should be in one now was a little disturbing.

'N..no Tom.'

'You don't sound very convincing. What have I done?'

'Nothing! Really! It's just...just...well, here we are heading back to Mr and Mrs Dodds' comfortable farmhouse. They'll spoil us with a lovely farmhouse tea, a warm fire and news of all they've been doing on their farm and...and....'

'And?'

'And ...and we have little or no news to share with them. I've hardly seen you for the past few weeks, what with all your commitments.'

Thomas was silent. He'd been feeling rather guilty about this himself. 'I know Kate. I'm sorry.' He wrapped his arm around her shoulders.

She snuggled in as they walked. 'I love you Thomas.' she said quietly.

'And I love you Kate.' he replied. He'd said it to her countless times over the past three months as his attraction had deepened into love, but somehow this afternoon, with the leaves falling and the onset of winter just around the corner, he was beginning to realise how empty and colourless his life would be without her. He loved his work as a Methodist local preacher and leading the cottage prayer meetings. He found working in the Bainbridge's drapery store with his brother, Cuthbert and his father, exciting and challenging. He was absorbed in farming and passionate over the Temperance Movement, but most of all he loved Kate Benson and nothing seemed quite so interesting when she wasn't around.

'I think we should do something about it, don't you Kate?'

'Oh Thomas, I couldn't bear it if you gave up some of your interests for me.'

'I wasn't actually thinking of giving anything up Kate.'

'Oh? Well Tom, I'm not the busy one.'

'I know. That was why I thought it would be a good idea if you came with me to a few of my activities. Then we could see more of each other.'

'Yes, I could do that.' Kate said hesitantly. Her brow furrowed and they walked on in silence for a while.

'Or I have a better idea.' Thomas said quietly.

'What's that?'

'You could marry me then I'd see you every day.'

Kate stopped and turning, stared up at Thomas's smiling face. 'Are you serious Tom?'

'Of course I am.' His grin widened. 'Oh Kate, you and I could do so much together.' He pulled her closer to him and she rested her forehead against his cheek. 'Nothing is quite the same without you around Kate. I can't even concentrate on Prayer Meetings these days. My mind keeps wandering back to you. I wonder what you're doing and when I'll see you next.' He gave her a squeeze. 'Please Kate. Marry me?' He held her close to him. He could feel the warmth of her body through her thick winter coat and her nose was cold against his chin but she was silent - frighteningly silent.

Thomas swallowed hard as fears and uncertainties drifted into his mind. *What if she said no!* Life without Kate was unthinkable! They could never go back to being just friends after this! What if she didn't love him as much as he thought she did? No! Oh dear God no! He couldn't take her rejection!

'Kate?' His voice was barely above a whisper. Why was she so silent. Why wasn't she responding. 'Kate?' He rested his hands on her shoulders and moved her gently away from him so he could see her face.

'Oh Thomas! Her blue eyes were filled with tears, her cheeks were wet but her face was radiant. 'I thought you'd never ask me. Yes my dearest. I will marry you.'

Thomas never thought he could experience such an overwhelming surge of happiness. I thought....I was frightened you didn't.... Oh Kate! Oh my dear Kate!' He pulled her to him again and held her tightly, not knowing whether to laugh or cry.

'We need to celebrate Kate. What shall we do?'

'There will be plenty celebrations in the weeks ahead Tom, but do you know what I'd like to do? Just the two of us. Now?'

'No What?'

'Have some home made jam, freshly baked bread and a pot of tea at Mrs Dodds.'

She pulled herself away from him, her face flushed with happiness. Then taking a few steps back, turned suddenly. 'Come on Tom! Race you back to the farmhouse!'

******

Miss Elisabeth Smith was beginning to wish she'd never set eyes on The Bible & Tract Depot. There had been nothing but hard work since she had moved in! Not that she was afraid of hard work but decorating the ceilings and the walls of her two rooms had been very demanding. On top of which, setting up the book shop at No.17 Pilgrim Street, had been harder work than she'd anticipated. As for those two stupid girls, Miss Grigs and

Miss Stephenson, they had been no help whatsoever! In fact they had been responsible for causing most of the disasters! Elisabeth Smith sat down shakily on the wooden chair behind the counter. It had all taken its toll. Her head ached and she couldn't stop shivering, despite the fact that Mary Jane had lit the fires and it was comfortably warm in the shop.

Hannah Grigs surveyed her depositary curiously. 'Are you all right Miss Smith?' Miss Smith *never* sat down, nor did she expect her staff to either, unless it was during their mid-day break in the basement.

'Just a little hot Miss Grigs.' she answered dabbing her forehead with a handkerchief.

'You don't look at all well. Why don't you go and lie down for a while? I can manage the shop.'

'Oh don't fuss girl! I'm perfectly all right! One cannot go taking a mid-day nap because of a mild fever.' She patted her neck and returned shakily to her feet. 'Now! Have you found space for those Ancient and Modern Hymnbooks? Goodness only knows why it's in such demand, but there you are. Ours not to reason why, etc.' She sat down again suddenly as a wave of dizziness washed over her.

Hannah Grigs put the armful of books she was carrying on to the table and hurried to her side. 'Mary Jane look after the shop. I'm taking Miss Smith to her room.'

Hannah's voice sounded a distance away yet she was aware she was by her side.

Mary Jane looked up from the parcel she was wrapping. 'Who me? I can't serve customers.'

'Yes you can. Don't argue.' Hannah said firmly, then Miss Smith felt herself being assisted to her feet.

'No Miss Grigs! No!' she protested weakly. 'There's too much to do. I have to order all the Christmas stock, then inform the Sunday School Superintendents that their books and cards have arrived. Besides which, Mr Smythe is in London so I cannot leave the shop unattended....' she trailed off.

'With all due respect Miss Smith, you are not well. I shall do it!'

Elisabeth Smith suddenly felt too faint to argue and surprised even herself by allowing the girl to assist her up the stairs to her two first floor rooms.

Hannah opened the door and was quite shocked at the condition of her depositary's living quarters. The room had been neatly whitewashed and wallpapered but there was a smell of dampness, there were no curtains up at the window or carpets on the floor and it was bitterly cold. November was a time for fires but ashes from the previous night still lay in the grate and there was a muddle of groceries and crockery around the stove. The bedroom wasn't much better. It too had been neatly whitewashed and wallpapered but unpacked boxes and furniture circled the unmade bed.

Miss Smith sank down on the edge of her bed shivering. 'I ...I wonder if I could...er..could trouble you to fill my hot water bottle please Miss Grigs.' Her words were heavy and laboured, whether from a temperature or having to step out of character and ask help of another human being, Hannah wasn't sure.

'Yes of course.' Hannah stooped to pick up the stone hot water bottle from the floor. 'I'll heat the kettle on the basement stove rather than up here so I can check on Miss Stephenson. I won't be long.'

She raced down the stairs and into the shop where to her surprise she discovered Mary Jane had positioned herself behind the counter and had combed her hair and discarded her pinny. Hannah grinned at her.

'Well done. Have you had a customer yet?'

Mary Jane shook her head and twisted her face. 'And I shall just faint if I do.'

'No you won't.' Hannah said firmly. 'I can't have both you and Miss Smith fainting on me. Just serve the customers like you've seen us do. Meanwhile, you can help by putting those Ancient and Modern Hymnbooks, neatly on to that shelf over there. I won't be long.'

By rights, Hannah knew it was her place to be behind the counter and Mary Jane should be the one heating the kettle on the gas stove in the basement, but there was something rather touching about the effort her friend had made to be a shop girl.

Five minutes later, Hannah was returning from the basement with the hot water bottle when she heard the shop door bell as a customer entered. She was tempted to take over from Mary Jane, but on the spur of the moment remained hidden by the basement door, listening to the gentleman's request.

'Do you have a copy of "Pilgrim's Progress" please?'

Hannah grinned to herself. "Pilgrim's Progress" were among the few words that Mary Jane could read.

'Yes sir.' Mary Jane answered confidently. 'Is it the hard back copy you

51

was wantin' or the cheap copy?'

'Oh er.. the hard back copy please. It is a birthday present for my niece.'

'All right, but mind you, the cheap copy will probably say just the same words.'

The gentleman smiled kindly at her. 'It probably will but I think I prefer the hard back copy as a gift.'

She listened to Mary Jane politely conversing with the customer while she wrapped the book and counted the change and when the gentleman had left, Hannah came on to the shop floor.

'There you are! I said you could do it.' she said triumphantly. 'Just a few more minutes behind the counter please Mary Jane, until I deliver this hot water bottle.'

When she reached the first floor, Hannah knocked on the door then entered. Miss Smith was lying in her bed with only the top of her head showing and Hannah was concerned to see the bedclothes shaking. The lady obviously had a very high temperature. 'Shall I light a fire and make you a cup of tea Miss Smith?'

Elisabeth shook her head. The last thing she wanted was someone prying around her muddled kitchen for tea and cups. 'You better not leave the shop floor unattended for t...too long Miss G..Grigs. Goodness only knows w...what Miss S...Stephenson will get up to in your absence.' Sick as she was, the thought crossed her mind that there was just as much likelihood of another disaster caused by Miss Grigs herself as by Miss Stephenson!

'I don't like the look of her at all.' Hannah confided to Mary Jane when they were alone in the shop together. It's freezing up there and she's got a high temperature but she won't let me light a fire or make her a cup of tea.'

Mary Jane chuckled. 'Can you blame her? She probably thinks we'll either drown her or set fire to her again.'

By half past five, the gas lamps had been alight for a couple of hours and Hannah was tidying the shop in preparation for closing. 'I think I shall ignore what the old battle-axe says and make her a cup of tea before I go home anyway.' she said to Mary Jane. 'Watch the shop again for me would you?'

Within seconds the errand girl's pinny and cap had been disposed of, her hands washed, her hair combed and she'd taken up her temporary position behind the counter again.

A rasping cough greeted Hannah as she knocked on the door with the cup of tea, but the invitation to enter was so weak she hesitated in case she had been mistaken.

The room was almost in total darkness. If it hadn't been for the gas lights on Pilgrim Street, she wouldn't have been able to see her depositary who was still lying in her bed shivering.

'I brought you a cup of tea Miss Smith.' she whispered. Her shoes echoed on the bare floorboards as she crossed the room.

'Thank you Miss Grigs. Tha...that is s.....so kind of you.' The voice was faint and shaking.

'Would you like me to light your fire before I go home? It's bitterly cold.'

'N....no thank you. I shall do that l....later myself when I m....make a meal.'

Hannah placed the cup and saucer on the small table beside the bed. 'Is there anything else I can do for you?'

'Just make s.....sure you lock up when you .....leave the shop.'

'Yes Miss Smith." Reluctantly Hannah sidled slowly backwards out of Miss Smiths two small rooms. Goodness only knows there'd never been much love lost between them but somehow it seemed cruel leaving her without a hot meal, a fire or a few lights. She said as much to Mary Jane as she prepared to leave the shop.

'She'll be up and giving us a mouthful come tomorrow, you mark my words.' Mary Jane retorted, 'Then you'll be wishin' you hadn't wasted all that sympathy.'

'But she looked really bad Mary Jane.' Hannah bit her lip worriedly. 'Still, if she doesn't want help, there's nothing we can do about it I suppose.'

On more than one occasion through the night, Mary Jane was woken by the rasping cough from Miss Smith's living quarters below theirs. Even Annie, normally a sound sleeper, had been disturbed by it.

'I think I'll knock and see if she wants some of our porridge.' Annie said the following morning as she stood at the stove ladling out porridge from their big pan. 'Howay our John, eat up now or you'll be late for school.'

'She won't thank you for it ma.' Mary Jane said ladling a bowlful out for herself.

They ate in silence, disturbed by the rasping cough coming from the rooms below. The cough had grown weaker throughout the night and Mary Jane's conscience had begun to prick her. Perhaps she shouldn't be so hard on the old battle-axe! After all she was working in a shop that sold Christian books and Bibles so perhaps she ought to be showing a little of what she sold, a bit of Christian love and compassion. Although in Miss Smith's case, it would take a *lot* of Christian love and compassion. But then The Bible & Tract Depot Committee had shown her and her family nothing but kindness. She had been given a job, some rooms to rent and Mr Richardson gave her John a place in his Ragged School? She made a sudden decision.

'Is there enough porridge to take her a little bowlful ma?'

Annie smiled at her daughter. 'Make it a big bowlful lass and take her a cup of tea as well.'

Mary Jane knocked on the door but didn't wait for the call to enter otherwise the porridge and tea would get cold. She struggled through the door with both hands full, carefully watching she didn't spill the tea in the saucer.

'Me ma sent this porridge.....' She glanced up. Miss Smith lay in her bed shivering, her eyes red, her face deathly white, her breathing coming in short sharp rasps. Her hair, normally in a neat bun, hung in an untidy mess across her face and shoulders. Obviously she'd been tossing and turning all night as half her bedcovers had fallen on the floor. Mary Jane shivered. The rooms were freezing, especially with no carpets on the floors or curtains up at the windows and judging from the cinders in the grate, there hadn't been a fire in it last night, nor a meal cooked on the small stove.

'I'll just leave it on the bedside table shall I?'

Elisabeth Smith could barely nod her head in acknowledgement let alone sit up and take nourishment.

Mary Jane hesitated. 'I think I better get me ma.' Leaving the breakfast on the nearest packing case she shot off upstairs. The warmth and comfort of their own two meagre rooms enveloped her welcomingly as she raced in through the door. 'Ma, I think you better come. She's in a bad way.'

Annie nodded. She wasn't surprised. Having lived most her life in Lower Pilgrim Street, she knew all about sickness and the sounds that had come from the lower floor had indicated a very poorly lady indeed. She wiped her hands on the towel and followed Mary Jane downstairs.

Miss Smith looked up at the unannounced entry but there was no recrimination in the pale blue eyes, just a silent plea for help. The two women looked steadily at each other for a moment then Annie put her hands on her hips and turned to her daughter.

'Mary Jane, go and tell our John to fetch a bucket of coal up here from the yard and to mind he doesn't scuff his shoes and to wash his hands a'fore school.' She moved over to the side of the bed and bending down said gently, 'Now then Miss, let's see if we can sit you up and give you some of this porridge. Mary Jane, put the kettle on the stove for a hot water bottle.' Very gently Annie placed her arm around Elisabeth's shaking shoulders and helped her sit up. She noticed she was still wearing her clothes from the previous day.

'The...there's the sh....shop to...to...'

Annie didn't even turn her head when she instructed, 'Mary Jane, go and open up the shop. Then tell our John he'll have to fetch another bucket of coal for the shop fire!' She sat on the edge of the bed and, picking up the bowl, spooned a small amount of porridge into Elisabeth's mouth.

'Th...thank you....'

'Shush now.' Annie said gently. 'Just you get this down you, then we'll light the fire and warm you up.'

Elisabeth had never been beholden to anyone before. She'd always been in control, self-sufficient, keeping a safe distance between herself and the rest of humanity. But suddenly she found herself being all those things she detested most in others. Weak, helpless, needy and having to allow her privacy to be invaded. Yet, gratefully, she took comfort from the warm porridge as it slid down her sore throat. When she'd eaten as much as she was able, Annie began to undress her nd Elisabeth Smith was so ill she just surrendered to Annie's instructions without argument or embarrassment. She even consented to Annie rubbing her chest with some strong-smelling liniment which, she was assured, would loosen up her chest and make it easier for her to breathe. Some time later she dozed off into a fitful sleep.

It seemed to Elisabeth, as though the days and nights that followed merged into a haze. Between the tossing and turning, the high temperatures and chest pains she was vaguely aware of the doctor calling and whispered conversations in the other room. Every so often John arrived carrying buckets of coal into her bedroom for the fire, or Mary Jane fed her a few mouthfuls of broth, and Annie seemed to be always there, washing and caring for her. In her more lucid moments she wondered how the shop was

55

doing but when her temperature soared, she would find herself rambling and unable to recognise her present surroundings.

Then one day it seemed as though the world came back into focus for Elisabeth Smith. She opened her eyes. It was growing dark outside and through the deep pink curtains that had been hung up at her bedroom window she was conscious of the first snow of winter falling softly on the roofs of Pilgrim Street. Her bedroom glowed red with the warmth of the fire crackling comfortingly in the hearth. Slowly she turned her head. Her furniture was neatly arranged around the room, mats were on the floor and her clothes had been hung in the wardrobe and stored in her chest of drawers. There was the sound of humming coming from the other room and a clatter of pans as someone made the evening meal. Then Annie stood at her bedroom door smiling as she wiped her hands on her pinny.

'So you're awake at last. How are y' feeling?'

Elisabeth licked her dry and parched lips. 'Better I think.' she whispered.

Annie nodded. 'Aye. You've been real bad Miss, You have that.'

'How...how long have......'

'Canny few days and I reckon it'll take a canny bit longer to get you back to normal. Now, how about a ham shank and some peas pudding?'

'I'm not...very hungry.'

'Aye, I know, but better belly burst than good food spoil and the soup from the shank'll do you good.'

It did do her good. So did the small helping of suet pudding and onion sauce she had to force down the day after, but she had been so ill it was a few more days before she was able to walk through into her living room and only then with the aid of Annie. The transformation made her gasp as Annie sat her in the chair by the fire with a blanket around her.

'It...it's lovely!'

'Aye. You're right cosy here now, Miss.'

The two women surveyed the results of Annie and Mary Jane's hard work. Her large rug had been laid out on the floor almost covering the bare floorboards, her lovely blue curtains had been hung and judging from the length, Annie had even gone to the bother of altering them for her. Her ornaments, pictures and books had been neatly placed on the shelves and mantelpiece and even her brass fender and fire irons had been polished. Annie had placed her lace-edged tablecloth over the table and set out her china tea service for their afternoon tea. Elisabeth smiled weakly at the woman.

'I...I am so...so very grateful to you.'

Annie grinned and embarrassed, quickly changed the subject. 'Aye, ...well....This is a nice set of cups and saucers and I've baked a few scones as a special treat for your first afternoon up.' She ran the edge of her pinny around one of the china teacups on the table. 'So ...so..I'll make the tea now eh?'

******

The absence of Miss Smith on the shop floor had made life extremely difficult for the staff of The Bible & Tract Depot. The weeks leading up to Christmas were usually one of the busiest times of the year for them. Hannah's sister, Ruth had come in to help them, as had Mr Henry Richardson, although if truth be told he was more of a hindrance than a help, being more interested in reading books than selling them. Unfortunately, Mr Smythe had been forced to spend valuable time with publishers in London and Leeds, so Ephraim Lister had been called upon to resume some of his old duties and teach Hannah how to order stock and deal with the money. One or two members of the Committee had also managed to squeeze a couple of hours of their valuable time into helping The Bible & Tract in their staffing crisis, but their greatest asset had been Mary Jane, who, after attending to her normal duties, donned her one and only "best frock" and helped out serving the customers. Not an easy task when you can barely read or write. Her efforts did not go unnoticed by the Committee - or by Miss Smith.

It was almost Christmas before Elisabeth Smith was permitted by Annie to take a walk in the fresh air and only then because the snow had cleared and ithe weather was into a warmer spell. It was such a lovely walk. The windows of Fenwick's, in Northumberland Street, were decorated for the coming festive holiday and there was an air of excitement as shoppers hustled around buying gifts but Elisabeth wasn't looking for the sort of gift you could buy in the shops. Instead, she made her way to the apartment of Miss Margaret Wilson, former depositary of The Bible & Tract Depot. The good lady was surprised when she answered the knock on her door and saw her visitor but, as was Miss Wilson's custom, she welcomed Miss Smith warmly and that afternoon, over a cup of tea and a slice of fruit

57

cake, they had a very constructive discussion.

******

The fire in the Committee room had roared away cheerily until well after the Committee members had left, but Henry Richardson and Joseph Maher were in no hurry to be away. They rested comfortably in the big armchairs either side of the fire, silently watching the flames flicker in the hearth. Joseph Maher broke the silence first. 'It was a good Committee Meeting this afternoon Henry.' he said thoughtfully. He took off his spectacles and began polishing them on his handkerchief. 'But it did make me wonder.'

Only the slightest twitch of the eyebrow gave any indication that Henry had heard him but it was enough to encourage Mr Maher to continue. 'Using these premises as a temporary holding area to send clothing to France for the War Victims Fund is an excellent idea. Excellent! However I feel we need to remind ourselves that our main purpose for setting up The Bible & Tract Depot was not charity work but to reach the ignorant and poor in our society with God's Word.' He continued polishing his spectacles in silence for a moment before he asked, 'Do you really think we are fulfilling what we set out to do Henry?'

Henry Richardson shifted the position of the cushion on his armchair. 'Mm'

Warming to his theme, Mr Maher went on, 'I mean, we sell books, hand out tracts and supply Sunday School material to churches but recently I've been questioning whether we are succeeding in reaching the common folk. Are we really having a Christian influence in their part of the city? Is it worth all this hard work?' Joseph Maher replaced his spectacles and rested back in his armchair watching the flames.

Henry Richardson stifled a yawn and was quiet for such a long time Joseph Maher thought he had dozed off, but that wouldn't have surprised him. Henry had found it necessary to withdraw from some of his more active commitments due to ill health and old age recently, but that was before the onset of Miss Smith's illness. Since then he'd been more active than ever.

'Those thoughts have occasionally crossed my mind too.' he said slowly.

Joseph Maher leaned forward and threw a log on the fire. 'I wonder if there is anyone walking around who can honestly say this shop has made a difference to their life. Anyone! Wouldn't it make you feel the financial risks we have taken and all the hard work we've all put into this place, has been worth while?' He leaned back against his chair again and smiled. 'But then my dear friend,' he said quietly, 'I'm afraid that's something we'll never know. I'm getting old Henry. I'm rambling like an old man.'

Silence returned to the warm committee room. Silence, except for the fire which crackled loudly as it wrapped itself around the log, Joseph Maher had thrown on the fire.

From a draughty shop doorway across the road, Ted Stephenson watched the sparks fly out of the chimney pot and into the clear star filled sky. He rubbed his hands together and stamped his frozen feet in an attempt to keep warm. Gradually his eyes dropped to the windows of the top floor where he knew Annie and his children would be laying the table for their evening meal.

'Ee, mam, I can hardly believe it!' Mary Jane's eyes brimmed with tears of happiness as she curled up on the little stool by the fire. 'Me being sent to night school to learn to read and write! It's the best Christmas present ever!'

Annie laughed and leaving her steaming pan of stew, moved over to her daughter to give her a big hug. 'Ee, pet. I'm that happy for you. Have you told Samuel yet?' Annie noted with some amusement that Mary Jane looked quite coy at the mention of Samuel's name. 'No. But I'm seeing him later tonight. I'll tell 'im then.'

John looked up from the kitchen table where he'd been practising his writing. 'Tell 'im what?' Annie ruffled her son's hair affectionately. 'That you're not the only one going to school - nosey. Miss Smith told the Committee about Mary Jane's hard work in the shop while she was ill and they have decided to promote our Mary Jane to shop girl. She goes to Miss Wilson's night schools for girls to learn her to read and write. Miss Smith set it all up for her.'

John's eager young face with its distinctive birthmark beamed up at his sister. 'A shop girl! Mary Jane that means you'll be gettin' eight whole shillings a week - like Miss Grigs! Wow! We'll be rich!'

Annie laughed but as she turned to the stove to stir her pan of stew a shadow of sadness crossed her face. The Bible &Tract Depot had been good to her family. They had a roof over their heads, work, schooling and their self-respect back. But why did she feel so sad.

On the floor below, Miss Elisabeth Smith sat comfortably by her fire with the gas lamp flickering upon her sewing. She smiled to herself. A rare occurrence, for Elisabeth Smith didn't often smile to herself but she had done more so more of late. She was looking forward to taking up the Committee's generous suggestion that she take a holiday, with pay, to recover from her illness. All she had to do now was find a suitable replacement while she was away. Perhaps Miss Grigs' sister, Ruth, would be willing to help out again? She would be a steadying influence in training Mary Jane in the shop. The whole of The Bible & Tract Depot had heard Mary Jane's squeals of delight when Mr Ephraim Lister told her she could become a shop girl and the Committee would pay for her tuition at Miss Wilson's evening school for girls. It gave Miss Smith a nice feeling to have set this up for Mary Jane. In some ways she was giving back a little of the love and compassion she had received from this family. She deposited her sewing on the chair and wandered over to the stove to put the kettle on for tea. On impulse, she flicked open the curtain and peered outside. It looked cold, cold enough for a frost. Folk were scurrying home to finish wrapping last minute Christmas presents. She spotted a familiar young couple staring in the jeweller's shop window and smiled to herself as she let the curtain drop. It was nice to be indoors, warm and comfortable, with the promise of friendship from Annie, from whom she'd learnt to share so much of herself and from Margaret Wilson, who had invited her to the Quaker church service on Christmas morning. It all promised a better Christmas than she'd had for years. Yes, Elisabeth thought. I'm pleased I took the position of depositary at The Bible & Tract Depot.

Meanwhile, outside the jewellery shop - Hannah Grigs and Ian Clarkson huddled together - staring at the glittering engagement rings through the window.

'They're very expensive.' Hannah said hesitantly.

'That's all right.' Ian spoke more confidently than he felt. He glanced up warily at the man standing in the shop doorway but although he was poorly dressed, he was clean shaven and didn't look as though he was out to rob anyone of their hard earned savings for an engagement ring.

'We won't have much money at first Hannah, but if Mr Bainbridge agrees to my training, I could very well be employed as one of the first missionaries to take the word of God to the farms and villages of

Northumberland in his Gospel Van. Are you sure you want that sort of life? I mean....'

Hannah silenced him with look, but it was one of absolute love and adoration. 'You will make a good missionary one day Ian,' she whispered, 'And I want nothing better than to stand by your side as your wife.' Their fingers entwined and in silence they continued staring through the window.

Ted Stephenson, had almost come out of the shadows of the shop doorway when he saw Mary Jane leave The Bible & Tract Depot, but he'd hesitated, uncertain, afraid almost and in that moment of hesitation a young man with a cloth cap pulled firmly over a crop of red hair called across to her.

'Mary Jane! Mary Jane!'

Ted had slunk back into the shadows again as his daughter had run across the road to greet her young man. It was Annie, that Ted Stephenson really wanted to see first. His Annie, living on the top floor of The Bible & Tract Depot, but he was afraid she would turn him away, and my God, didn't she have every right to after what he'd done? But he needed to see her. She might need money for the children. Not that he had much but since he'd picked up that tract at the Races and been going to the Mission Hall, he'd gradually been able to climb out of the pit of despair he'd been in. He had even found himself a job at the docks.

The shop lights were off. The Bible & Tract Depot had closed at seven o'clock and that other young girl, the tall willowy one, had locked up then rushed across the road to join her young man. A curtain had twitched on the first floor as someone peeped outside and the gas lamps still burned brightly in two of the other windows but ah! they flickered. Someone had turned them off.

Ted Stephenson watched the two well-dressed elderly gentlemen, who he recognised as members of the Committee, leave the premises. A woman was with them, opening the door for them, wishing them a 'Merry Christmas Sirs' and then they were gone. The woman stood with the front door open for a long time, just staring across the road - at him. He stared back. He had no courage to go over and see her and all those well rehearsed speeches to his Annie had deserted him.'

'Ted? I know it's you. Come over here and let's have a look at you!'

A horse and carriage clattered by and he had to wait until they had passed before he could cross the road. Then he stood before her like a shy

61

schoolboy. She didn't look so bad did his Annie. Her hair was greyer and there was scarring on her forehead but she had a new dress on and her eyes were smiling.

'Annie? Annie I...I....' There were no words to say sorry, to ask forgiveness, to say he still loved her, not yet at any rate. They would come later.

'Come on in Ted.' his wife said, opening wide the door of the shop. 'I've some soup on the stove and there's a warm fire. It's too cold a night to be hanging around outside.'

PART TWO
THE SHOP ON PILGRIM STREET
November 1901

'Good morning Mr Middleton.'

Robert Middleton looked up as a draught of street air swept across the shop floor sending flames flickering up the chimney. He was a smart, confident man in his mid-thirties, with a square face and deep brown eyes. His pleasant and direct manner had attracted the Committee to employ him as their new manager. They were a little anxious that the strain of being a widower with three young daughters to raise might prove too much, however the last few years had proved him more than efficient in filling Mr Ephraim Lister's, then Mr William Smythe's shoes in managing The Bible & Tract Depot.

'Good morning Mr Bainbridge.' He nodded to the two handsome boys who had entered with him. 'Mr Wilfred, Mr Lindsay. Can I help you?'

The older man's face fell. 'Ah! Then I gather Mrs Bainbridge has not visited the shop this morning? She and I had agreed to meet here before going shopping.' Thomas stroked his greying beard thoughtfully and Robert Middleton wondered why he hadn't learned, after thirty years of marriage to Kate, that when he arranged to meet her he should add an extra half hour on to his agreed meeting time. He had a deep respect for Thomas Bainbridge, who was now approaching sixty. Thomas and Kate had had a large family of eight children, two of whom were with him this morning, Following the death of his father Emerson in 1891, Thomas and his brother, George, had taken over the family drapery business, Bainbridge & Co. Ltd of Market Street. He was also Vice-Chairman of the Consett Iron Co., a director of Swan Hunter, the ship building company, a director of the Wallsend Slipway & Engineering Company, and a Justice of the Peace. He still retained a passionate involvement in the Temperance Movement, the Methodist church, local preaching, mission work, the Y.M.C.A., and never missed a meeting at The Bible & Tract Depot. In fact, so great had his influence in the city become that there were few functions at which he was not present. Every minute counted for Thomas Bainbridge and that Kate should be wasting any of them for him was most annoying!

As if sensing the impatient vibrations from her husband from afar, the door bell rang and Kate Bainbridge breezed into the shop. While her once trim figure had spread somewhat after eight children, the twinkle in her eye had not dimmed, nor had her enthusiasm that matched and supported Thomas in his work.

'Good morning Mr Middleton.' she smiled across at him before turning to her husband. 'I'm so sorry I'm late Thomas, but .....Wilfred! Leave those books alone!'

'I'm sorry Mr Middleton, they are full of mischief this morning.'

Robert Middleton moved forward to pick up a book one of the boys had knocked off the shelf and Kate smiled graciously at him. 'Thank you Mr Middleton.' Then turning to Thomas and her two younger offspring demanded, 'Well? Are you gentlemen ready?'

It was as the Bainbridges left the shop amidst a babble of chatter that a young woman, attractive rather than pretty, entered. She was tall, almost as tall as he was, with a broad forehead and high cheekbones. She looked to be in her mid-twenties and wore a heavy winter coat.

'I understand I have to report to Mr Middleton for work?' Her manner was brusque but not unfriendly.

'I am Mr Middleton.'

She moved elegantly across the shop floor towards him.

'Ah, good morning Mr. Middleton! My name is Caroline Dickinson. The Trustees employed me last month to work in The Bible & Tract Depot. I believe you were purchasing books in London at the time of my interview.'

He was sure it wasn't meant to be a criticism but it sounded like it. 'Yes! Yes, indeed I was informed about you Miss Dickinson.' He came from behind the counter and shook her hand. Her gloved fingers were warm to the touch. 'We are in rather a state of confusion I'm afraid.' he explained, 'Your immediate superior, Mr Harris has had a personal matter to attend to this morning and our young delivery girl hasn't, as yet, made an appearance. I'm afraid her time-keeping leaves a lot to be desired. However I will show you what your duties will be.'

Caroline Dickinson murmured, 'Thank you Mr Middleton.'

Self-consciously he began to outline what her work would entail, walking briskly around the shop floor pointing to bibles, prayer books, theological books, hymn books, Sunday School material and their small stationery business. He'd almost finished the tour when the shop door opened and a comfortably plump, middle-aged lady entered.

'Ah! Miss Grigs!' Relieved, Robert Middleton turned towards the newcomer. 'Let me introduce you to Miss Caroline Dickinson, our new employee.' The ladies nodded politely to each other. 'Miss Grigs is the sister of a former employee, Hannah Grigs, who married one of our colporteurs twenty years ago.' Robert explained. 'Miss Grigs occasionally steps in to help us when we're short-staffed. She will be able to point out what is required of you Miss Dickinson.' As if relieved to be out of her company, Robert Middleton reached for his heavy overcoat then turned to address the older woman. 'I shall be away most of the day Miss Grigs. I have one or two other errands to attend to. Oh! And when Mr Harris comes in this afternoon, could you ask him if he has spoken to the painter about washing the outside signboards and paint work. Perhaps it could be done before Christmas.' Robert Middleton fastened his coat and placing his hat on his head, gave both ladies a curt nod before hurrying out of the shop.

'Come my dear, let me take your coat and make you comfortable.' Ruth Grigs said companionably as soon as the door had closed. 'I bet his lordship gave you a rushed tour of the shop leaving you more confused than when you came in.'

Caroline smiled warily. 'Mr Middleton was er..very pleasant.' The last thing she wanted to do was gossip about her boss on her first day.

'You'll not have to mind him.' Ruth said hanging Caroline's coat up on the peg behind the counter. 'He's a hard worker but a fair man and he expects the same from his staff. Never misses a day's work, even with three young daughters on his hands, although mind you I believe his sisters-in-law help bring the girls up.' She sighed as she tidied a few books on the top of the counter. 'My sister Hannah and I know what it's like to be brought up with no mother. Poor little mites. Girls need a mother, don't you think so?' Caroline opened her mouth to reply but Ruth Grigs was in fine talking form that morning. 'Well enough of my chatter. Let me show you round properly so you know where everything is.'

Caroline was rather relieved when the rest of the staff appeared at mid-day and introduced themselves.

Mr Henry Harris, who had taken Miss Elisabeth Smith's post was her immediate superior. He was a thin, sharp-featured little man with rimmed pince-nez perched neatly on the edge of his nose. Thinning hair made him look older than his actual age and when he spoke it was with the quiet intonations of an undertaker, rather than a book-seller. According to Miss Jane Gibson, the fourteen-year old, bright eyed, freckled faced errand girl with unruly auburn hair, he was a kindly enough man who had shown the patience of saint with Miss Smith, who had continued to occupy the two upper rooms and insisted on locking up in the evening, right up to the time of her death. Before the lunch break was over Caroline knew everyone's life story, thanks to Jane Gibson's incessant chatter.

Mrs Richie, the cleaner and caretaker was a buxom woman with more chins than you could count and a face that looked as though it would crack if it smiled. Formally caretaker of St. James's Church, she had been warmly recommended by Annie Stephenson after Ted had found a labouring job and they had moved to Jarrow. Mrs Richie had gratefully taken up the vacant post of caretaker at two and sixpence per week, plus Miss Smith's two attic rooms with the free coal, gas and water. Annie's two rooms at the top of the house had been rented out as offices and meeting rooms to the North of England Temperance League.

'In fact,' Jane Gibson informed the new employee, 'Mary Jane Stephenson, the cleaner's daughter, got promoted from errand girl to shop assistant. That's like wot I'm gonna do, when I learns meself to read and write like! Oh yes! We are all encouraged in our education.' She beamed delightedly at Caroline, her auburn curls bouncing with enthusiasm. 'That's why I goes to night-school!' she added.

'Good for you!' Caroline encouraged. She liked Jane Gibson but couldn't help reflect that if The Bible & Tract Depot wanted the best work out of the staff, then Jane would have to curb her chatter and be more disciplined about her time-keeping.

At six o'clock that evening Caroline Dickinson left the warm little shop with its flickering gas lights and blazing fire and drawing her scarf tightly around her neck stepped out into the frosty November evening. The streets were busy. Horse-drawn trams with passengers shivering on the open tops clattered noisily by. A small group of policeman loudly and physically urged an even larger and rowdier group of young men into the elegant new Police Station. Shops in Pilgrim Street and Northumberland Street were closing for the evening, their staff hurrying home for their evening meal. It had been a busy but interesting day. A hand rested on her arm. Startled, she turned. It was Robert Middleton.

'Allow me to escort you across the road, Miss Dickinson. It is unusually busy this evening.'

'Er...Thank you.' she murmured. She was very conscious of his hand tucked underneath her elbow as he steered her across the busy road and was relieved when they reached the other side and he had stepped back.

'I hope you have enjoyed your first day with the Bible and Tract Depot,' he said conversationally. He appeared more sociable than earlier in the day.

She smiled reassuring. 'I have Mr Middleton, thank you.'

He touched the brim of his hat. 'Then I'll bid you good-night Miss Dickinson and look forward to seeing you tomorrow.' He smiled. He looked handsome when he smiled she thought.

'Goodnight.' she replied softly and watched him walk away.

He knew she was watching him as he turned and walked briskly down the road and for some strange reason it left him with a pleasant feeling. A very pleasant feeling indeed.

******

Jane Gibson, the delivery girl, always left her house in Elswick Road early in the morning because it was a long walk into the centre of Newcastle, where The Bible & Tract Depot stood. She liked the walk because there were gaps between the houses and she could look across the River Tyne to Gateshead, and the green fields and hills in the distance. Her brother Tom worked in Gateshead. He had to walk into Newcastle then cross the Swing Bridge to get to his place of work. Best of all she liked to look down at the Vickers factory where the big chimneys belched out smoke, most of it seeming to shroud Elswick Road in a fog all day if the wind was blowing in that direction, but Jane Gibson didn't mind. At least Vickers employed her da and there was money coming in the house again. In fact, what with both her father and Tom working and her six shillings a week from The Bible & Tract Depot, they were quite well-off compared to many families.

She liked her work as errand girl for The Bible & Tract Depot and she liked the people she worked with. Mr Middleton was nice, but he was often in London visiting publishers. Mr Harris, who was in charge when Mr Middleton was away, was a quiet patient man and only "tut-tutted" if she was late or dawdled with her deliveries. She had discovered Miss Dickinson could be a bit of a tartar if she found her chattering but, as she explained to Miss Dickinson, if she didn't talk the shop would probably be in silence all day!

The Committee were a bit awesome. Jane Gibson was scared of them. They all lived in big houses, had important jobs and pots of money but as long as you were dressed smartly and kept the shop tidy, other than saying 'Good morning', they left you alone. Apparently they weren't called "Committee Members" any more.

Mr Harris had explained. 'The Committee,' he said, 'have found it necessary to have a legal constitution so a Trust Deed, listing the aims, objectives and principles of The Bible & Tract Depot has been drawn up and a board of nine Trustees formed to govern the shop. These consist of gentlemen belonging to various denominations. Wesleyan, Baptist, Congregationalist, Primitive Methodist, Society of Friends and Methodist New Connection. Most of them are the same people. Mr Harris pointed out. 'They've just changed their name from "Committee" to "Trustees".'

'So will that affect my wages?' Jane had wanted to know.

Henry Harris had peered tolerantly at her over his pince-nez. 'No.' he patiently explained. 'It just means the bosses are getting themselves organised.'

Jane Gibson couldn't help wonder why they hadn't got themselves organised before now. Goodness me! They had been going for ever so many years! Good job Mr Middleton, Mr Harris, Miss Dickinson and herself knew what they were doing, otherwise the place would fold up!

Jane Gibson had a busy but interesting morning, but then it always was a busy and interesting morning when the Trustees had their meeting. She was expected to give Mrs Richie a hand lighting the fires in the big room where they met, and in the shop, as well keeping them stoked up for the rest of the day, which meant her legs ached with continually running up and down the stairs with buckets of coal. The maddening thing was that each time a Trustee appeared through the shop door the flames would flicker uncertainly and all the warm air would escape. Jane Gibson was cross! If this was going to happen every time a Trustee appeared, the place would never warm up! Had they no consideration?

Halfway through the morning John Stephenson arrived and gently closed the door behind him. She liked John.. A quiet, studious, friendly man who might have been quite attractive if it hadn't been for the disfiguring birth mark on his face. Perhaps that was why he had never married? Now in his early thirties he was working for the Newcastle Colporteur Society, and as he drew his books from the Bible and Tract Depot, he was often in the shop but never too busy to help her, a chattering fourteen year old girl, anxious to learn to read and write.

It was almost mid-day before Thomas Bainbridge, the first of the trustees, appeared from the morning's meeting.

'Ah! John!' Thomas left the door wide open as he came down the stairs. 'I wanted to have a word with you.'

Jane Gibson scowled at his back as she closed the door after him.

'Yes Mr Bainbridge. What can I do for you?'

Thomas steered him towards the tall shelves housing the stationery business at the back of the shop where they would be out of earshot, with the exception of Miss Jane Gibson, engrossed in dusting the shelves nearby.

'I thought I better inform you that the Trustees have been forced to send a letter to your employer, The Newcastle Colportage Society, drawing attention to the fact that almost all the purchases made by the colporteurs, yourself excluded I hasten to add, are made from the Society in Edinburgh, rather than here, in Newcastle. As the Newcastle Colporteur Society receive regular and generous donations from us we feel they should assist us all they can by purchasing books from our shop.' Thomas hesitated. 'We are conscious however, that our letter could leave you in a difficult position John.'

'Mm' John Stephenson chewed his lip worriedly. He didn't like the idea of being stuck in the middle of a disagreement between the Society he worked for and the shop who had befriended him.

'However,' Thomas Bainbridge continued. 'It occurred to us that having our own colporteur could aid the work of The Bible and Tract Depot.' John didn't fail to miss the twinkle that had appeared in Thomas Bainbridge's eyes. 'The man we employed would be called upon to visit the outlying country districts selling books and holding Cottage Prayer Meetings. It would enable us to keep closer contact with all our Sunday School teachers, buy larger quantity of books, secure better terms and during the shop's busy times we could call upon him for assistance.' Thomas hesitated for a moment before adding, 'We wondered if you would be interested in the position John?'

John's face flushed. 'Interested? Yes sir. I most certainly would!'

A slow smile spread across Thomas's face. 'I thought you would. Of course you would have to use one of the Gospel Vans?'

'I feel honoured to be asked sir.'

'Good! Good!'

Back in 1868, Thomas Bainbridge's inspiration in the use of horse-drawn caravans as mission centres to carry religious books, Bibles and tracts to the out-lying communities of Northumberland, had proved an enormous success. Many of these small country farming communities found it hard to raise enough money to build a chapel, so the Gospel Vans played an important role in building up and maintaining the Wesleyan faith. After John Stephenson had finished his schooling he'd become a Christian, then a Methodist local preacher, and had, on occasion, joined Thomas Bainbridge in leading the Cottage Prayer Meetings, so the majority of the work being asked of him was familiar.

Jane Gibson left her dusting and, as unobtrusively as possible, crossed the shop to digest this latest piece of gossip. On her way she crossed paths with Mr Middleton who was striding over toward Mr Harris who was wrapping a book behind the counter. She abruptly changed direction, kneeling by the hearth to add more coal to the already well-stoked fire just so she could hear what was being said.

'Mr Harris, I thought I asked you to organise for the outside signboards to be washed!'

The pince-nez wobbled uncertainly on Mr Harris's nose. 'Oh Mr Middleton! I must apologise. It completely slipped my mind. There was so much to think about....but...but I shall see to it without delay.'

Robert Middleton grunted and his voice dropped when he asked, 'And the till? Have you checked it again Mr Harris?'

'Yes Mr Middleton. Three times. Miss Dickinson assisted me.' Mr Harris ran his finger around his collar. He appeared rather fraught. 'There is no doubt 13/6d is missing.'

Robert took a deep breath. 'It is less than two weeks since you were 10/2d short, then last week 5/6d was missing. Either your figures are incorrect or we are having money stolen!'

'I am really sorry Mr Middleton. I have no idea.....' The little man's face was red, either from embarrassment or Jane Gibson was stoking up the fire too high.

'Is there more trouble?' David Richardson, one of the trustees joined the two men. A large portly man with a good head for figures. He had taken over Joseph Maher's post as treasurer.

'Yes sir.' Robert Middleton replied soberly. 'I'm afraid we're now missing 13/6d from the till.'

'You've checked and double checked Mr Harris?'

Henry Harris looked decidedly uneasy. 'Yes sir. I'm afraid we have to come to the conclusion that money is being stolen.'

David Richardson rubbed his chin. All three men appeared very troubled. 'This is a most unpleasant business. Is the till ever left unattended Mr Harris?'

'Not if we can help it sir. Although there are occasions when one of us may be at the back of the shop seeing to the stationery side of the business.'

'It er....could not be...' he glanced around him but failed to see Jane Gibson on her knees by the fire. 'It could not be a member of staff?'

'Oh certainly not!' Robert Middleton spoke up vehemently. 'I have no doubt they are all honest and trustworthy.'

'Quite so! Quite so!' David Richardson thoughtfully continued rubbing his chin. After a short pause he said, 'Perhaps our policy from today ought to be for members of staff to make sure one of their number is always present at the front shop. Can you organise that Mr Harris?'

'Yes sir. I will indeed and my sincere apologies. I cannot understand what has happened. I can only assume that someone, noticing a member of staff not at the counter, took advantage of the situation. However I will ensure it does not happen again.'

David Richardson smiled at the worried furrow over Mr Harris's brow. 'Don't over concern yourself Mr Harris.' he said kindly. 'These things happen.' He turned to Robert Middleton. 'Now, I really must draft out those grants. I have no problem writing a cheque for £50 to The Newcastle Bible Society and The Newcastle Sunday School Union, but I do have a few reservations with the Newcastle Colportage Society, with the way things stand at the moment.' David Richardson ascended the stairs to the office muttering to himself, leaving Mr Harris still wringing his hands.

This matter of money missing from the till had upset him more than he cared to admit and he couldn't get it out of his mind for the rest of the morning. It couldn't possibly be a member of staff could it? No! Definitely not! The trouble was, something like this left you suspicious of everyone. Perhaps it was one of their regular customers? He glanced warily at each customer as they entered the shop. Most of them were familiar faces and other than a few well dressed strangers browsing around the shelves, the shop was remarkably quiet.

It was then he heard the whispered conversation behind the tall shelves at the back of the shop. His muscles tensed. Since they'd brought in those tall shelves for the stationery business anybody could lurk behind them just waiting for him to move away from the till. Stealthily he tiptoed across the shop floor so he could have a closer look. Poking his head around the corner he was amazed to see Mr Middleton and Miss Dickinson with their heads bent closely together over a book. He coughed politely and they both started.

'Oh - Mr Harris, have you seen this book?' Robert Middleton took a step back like a schoolboy caught in the act of doing something naughty.

'What book would that be Mr Middleton?' he answered stiffly.

'Miss Dickinson has discovered a book written many years ago by the first manager of the shop, Mr Ephraim Lister, entitled "Moralising in Verse." It must have been hiding at the back of these shelves for years.'

'Mm. Interesting. Very interesting.' As he turned away to serve a customer he could not help but reflect that that wasn't the only thing that had been found hiding at the back of the shelves! 'It wouldn't do to forget your appointment with Mr Lamb, Mr Middleton.' he reminded his manager.

'Oh yes. Thank you, Mr Harris.' Robert Middleton reluctantly dragged himself away from the comfortable position of looking over Miss Dickinson's shoulder and struggled to focus his mind on Mr Lamb.

Mr Lamb was a shrewd businessman who had refused to take less than £110 a year for the lease of building which housed The Bible & Tract Depot. The Trustees felt this was a gross amount considering the work they had done to the premises and Robert Middleton was requested to call upon him to discuss the matter. However, as he strode purposefully down Grainger Street a few minutes later, his thoughts were not on the lease, nor the missing money, but on Miss Caroline Dickinson. Never in his wildest dreams had he imagined he could be attracted to another woman after the death of his dear wife, but every morning there'd been a spring in his step on his way to work. Even during his London trips, a time he normally enjoyed as he loved the capital city, he'd found his mind continually returning to her and a longing to be back in the north-east to see her again. It was only as he entered Mr Lamb's office that it dawned on him that possibly, just possibly, he was in love for the second time in his life.

******

It was John Stephenson who spotted the boy first. A scruffy little urchin peering at the display of books in the window. Probably an occupant of one of the poorer houses on Lower Pilgrim Street, John thought. As he watched him from across the road, memories of his own poor and violent childhood rose to the surface. If it hadn't been for the kindness of Henry Richardson, the Lord alone knows what he'd be doing now! He was just about to cross over to speak to the boy when a customer left the shop. As the door opened and the bell tinkled, the little chap was through the gap as quick as a flash and had disappeared somewhere inside the shop. Curiously, John crossed the road and followed him into the Bible and Tract Depot.

'Good morning John.' Jane Gibson staggered across the shop floor with a pile of books in her arms.

'Here, let me help you.' He relieved her of the books and looked around. There was no sign of the boy anywhere.

'What's wrong?' Jane asked.

He steered her into the corner of the room behind the tall bookcase. 'Did you see a young boy come into the shop?' he whispered.

Jane frowned thoughtfully. 'No, cos I was upstairs getting them books. Why like?'

'Well he's here somewhere. I saw him peering through the window and as soon as a customer left he sneaked through the open door.'

'Where is he then?'

'I don't know.' John whispered. 'I followed him in here, but with money being taken from the till.......'

Henry Harris panted as he came down the stairs from the office. He didn't like stairs. His legs were too short for stairs. He glanced at his watch. Miss Dickinson would be back from her lunch break shortly. Just as well. He was ready to take his. He glanced at the empty counter and growled under his breath. How many times had he told that dizzy girl, Jane Gibson to stay beside the till if he and Miss Dickinson were otherwise occupied. Really! She was most unreliable! He tilted his head. Were those whispers he could hear behind the tall shelves at the back of the room? It couldn't be Mr Middleton and Miss Dickinson. She was on her lunch break and he was in London for three days. Nervously he glanced at the till and his heart lurched. It was slightly open as if someone had touched it. He looked back towards the tall shelves then slowly, so that his shoes did not squeak, he tiptoed across the shop floor. The whispering stopped as if they had heard his approach. He hesitated, then cautiously poked his head around the corner. Heavy hands landed on his shoulders and he felt his feet lifted off the ground.

'Aahh!!' He let out a cry of alarm and was dropped almost immediately.

John Stephenson looked suitably embarrassed. 'Mr Harris sir. I'm sorry! I thought you were....'

'What do you think....! Henry Harris began loudly then saw both his colporteur and delivery girl had fingers to their lips. 'What is it?' he whispered.

'There's someone in the shop.' Jane whispered.

'I should hope so.' he said flatly. 'Otherwise we'd never sell anything.'

'No. A young lad. I saw him sneak in and he's disappeared. John explained quietly.

'It's hardly a banqueting hall. He can't be far.'

'What's a...a banqueting ....there!' Jane pointed to the heavy cloth covering the display table at the front of the window. It had moved very slightly.

All three slowly crossed the shop floor towards the window, fanning out ready to catch the intruder. Suddenly the shop bell tinkled and the door opened as Caroline Dickinson returned from her lunch break. Quick as a flash the young lad scuttled from his hiding place to make his getaway.

'Oh no you don't.' For the second time that morning the heavy hands of John Stephenson landed on shoulders. 'Now what have you been up to?'

The small figure squirmed, his feet thrashing the empty air. 'I dun nofin'. Honest mister!' The boy's jacket was too small for him. His shoes too big, hair too long and he didn't smell too good either. Caroline Dickinson wrinkled her nose.

'What on earth is going on here?' she demanded.

John shook the boy and coins fell out of his hand and rolled across the shop floor. 'I think we may have found our thief Miss Dickinson.'

'I just wanted to buy me dinner.' the boy wailed.

John set him on his feet then bent down and looked him squarely in the face. 'And how often have you played that little prank?' he said firmly.

The boy shrugged, his eyes wide with fear as he stood surrounded by his captors.

'How often?' John demanded and gave the boy a shake.

'A few times.' the boy muttered.

'I think I shall call a constable.' Caroline said making her way towards the door.

The boys eyes grew wide with fear. 'No! Not the coppers!'

'What's your name boy?' Henry Harris asked.

'Patrick Fisher.' The boy shuffled in his large shoes.

'And you live down there?' John pointed in the direction of Lower Pilgrim Street.

'Aye. How do you know that?'

'I... just.... know!' John stood up. He was an impressive figure of a man and Patrick Fisher was obviously impressed. The boy visibly shook and Caroline hesitated.

'Not the coppers!' he whined.

'Where's the money you stole out of the till today?' John demanded.

Patrick rummaged in his coat pocket and brought out two more coins. 'Is that it?'

The boy nodded. 'Divvint tell the coppers!' he pleaded.

John Stephenson glanced at Henry Harris. 'No coppers.' the man said softly.

John reached into his own pocket and pulled out three coins. 'That,' he said handing them to the boy. 'Is for your dinner.' Then bending down he growled into the boy's startled face, 'But I warn you, if we catch you stealing in this shop again, I shall have the coppers on you! I know where you live. Do you understand?'

The boy nodded. The bell on the door tinkled as Caroline Dickinson opened it for him and as quickly as he'd entered the shop, the boy departed.

Jane Gibson gazed at John Stephenson. 'You was wonderful!' she said in admiration and John, totally unused to such flattery, had the grace to blush.

'Well done Mr Stephenson. Well done indeed!' The relief of having found his thief was quite apparent in Mr Henry Harris.

'As long as he doesn't come back!' Caroline said warily. 'Perhaps you were a little lenient on him Mr Stephenson. A child like that has no sense of right and wrong.'

John Stephenson almost opened his mouth to argue. He knew all about being a "child like that", but he decided, as Jane Gibson was still looking at him so adoringly, that he wasn't going to argue. He'd much rather have Jane Gibson's adoration.

******

Saltwell Park in Gateshead, was a mass of crocuses and daffodils during the Easter week, thanks mainly to an unusually warm spell of weather. The trees wore their first hazy light green leaves as buds struggled to break out of their protective winter coverings. Couples meandered slowly along the walkways, the ladies parading their new Easter bonnets and spring outfits.

Robert Middleton's three children ran ahead playing with their hoops, their cries of laughter echoed across the lake as they soaked in the first rays of the summer sun. His eldest daughter, Beth, kept a watchful eye on the younger ones, almost as if she sensed her father needed time to talk to this lady he'd brought home to tea to meet them.

Robert Middleton glanced down at Caroline walking by his side. He had never seen her look so lovely.

'Caroline.' He spoke her name gently and she lifted her face to his, her lips parted and she smiled.

'Yes?'

He entwined his fingers behind his back as he walked. 'If the children have seemed a little...er...aloof, I hope you will forgive them.' he said. 'They have been through a lot, losing their mother and I think they're a trifle confused over er.... over my reasons for inviting you for tea.'

'Oh!' They walked in silence for a while. 'Why did you invite me to tea?' she asked.

'I er....' He wasn't very good at these sort of conversations. 'I thought it would be nice for the children to meet the people I work with.'

'Ah!' A smile played around her mouth. 'I didn't see the rest of the shop staff at the tea table.'

He knew she was teasing him. 'Yes...well...' He twiddled his fingers behind his back embarrassed. He was losing his grip on this conversation. 'Yes, well...er... I have no romantic interest in either Mr Harris, Miss Gibson or Mr Stephenson.' he remarked dryly.

The hoop rolled in their direction and landed at Caroline's feet, followed by a breathless Beth with her fair hair falling in her face. 'Sorry!' she gasped picking up the hoop. She glanced quickly at her father and then Caroline before flashing them a smile and rushing off to join the younger children.

'A romantic interest?' Caroline reflected back at him.

'Yes.' He hesitated and he was sure she must be able to hear his heart thumping. 'I have been so...so very happy since you came to work at The Bible & Tract Depot, Caroline. I never thought I would know such happiness again.' He watched her face anxiously for any hint of rejection but her hazel eyes looked up at him and her face spoke in a way words would never be able to. It gave him the courage to say, 'I love you Caroline.' He released his twitching fingers from behind his back and encircling her fingers, drew her hand through his arm. She didn't resist.

'And I love you too Robert.' She said it in such a matter of fact way that he felt he ought to have known it. Their path meandered through beds of daffodils.

'Caroline dear?' he hesitated.

'Yes Robert?'

'I er... I have three children.'

'That fact had not escaped my notice Robert. I have just had tea with them.'

For one so articulate he found it extremely irritating being lost for words. 'Would you.....could you....' Was it too soon to speak so boldly? 'Three children are a handful, but I was wondering Caroline, if........if....'

She squeezed his arm. 'They're lovely children Robert. I would love to get to know them better.'

'You would?'

'Yes I would.'

'Then perhaps you could come to tea next Sunday.' he said gently.

'I would like that very much.'

'And perhaps the week after and the week after that?' he smiled down at her.

'For as long as you like Robert dear.'

He was elated. Her reply made him want to shout and sing at the top of his voice. But not in a public place like Saltwell Park and not in front of the children. They were nearing the new pavilion - it was empty. Robert drew her into the shadow of its rafters and Mr Robert Middleton gently kissed Miss Caroline Dickinson, and she responded - in public!

******

He stood shivering at the graveside. Was it the cold or was it the shock of what had happened? Strange how his mind wasn't on the present, on what was going on around him. Perhaps that was his way of dealing with grief, blocking it out. He wanted to be angry. He wanted to shout and scream at somebody! Anybody! God even! Why should God take yet another precious life from him? Why? Surely the death of his first wife had been punishment enough? He'd thought he'd been blessed with a time of happiness when he married Caroline but now.....

The day he had made Caroline Dickinson his wife, the staff of The Bible & Tract Depot had been delighted that the romance had taken place under their very roof. The Trustees had been more than generous. Firstly they'd presented them with an extremely large cheque. Secondly they'd presented them with a fine china plate with the inscription:

To Mr and Mrs Robert Middleton from the Trustees of The Bible & Tract Depot, on the occasion of their marriage, in recognition of their long and valued service.

Finally, Thomas Bainbridge had asked the new Mrs Middleton if she would agree to travel to London rail with her husband, to help him in selecting stock.

'All expenses will be paid by us of course.' Thomas Bainbridge added.

Those had been the happy times. Even their London holiday had not seemed like work as he showed his new wife the sights of the capital city. With Caroline by his side he was the happiest man alive.

Robert found himself smiling at the memories. One didn't usually smile at a funeral of one so dear to him and that he should do so now when there were so many other emotions churning around inside him, was quite strange.

His faith wasn't helping him in the way he though it would. God seemed a million miles away - if He were there at all! The smile disappeared and the cold north-east wind seemed to suddenly chill him. He pulled his overcoat collar up around his neck, horrified that he should have allowed such a thought to penetrate his mind. Of course God was there - wasn't He? What if death was all there was? How could he cope with losing one so dear, never to see her again? He couldn't! He had to believe in something, someone! He had to! He gazed across the rows of gravestones to the valley beyond. A solitary crow squawked hungrily as it perched on a nearby tree. It looked like he felt. Lonely and empty. The funeral service in the church should have been the place to have said his good-byes, but he hadn't. How could he say good-bye to someone he loved so much? Dear God! He was so cold! So cold........

'Daddy?' A small hand slid into his own and Robert looked down at his son. He was a mirror image of himself with the same dark hair and brown eyes but with Caroline's straight stature and firm chin. He was too young to understand the meaning of death.

'Daddy, can we go home now?' he whispered.

Robert squeezed his hand harder than he intended. How could he leave this graveside? How?

'Ouch! Daddy, you're hurting my hand!'

'Sorry son.' The tears he'd held back for so long almost broke through that wall of reserve he'd erected. Oh God! He didn't want to cry! Not here. Not in public!

He felt her hand on his shoulder. The strength of her presence behind him. 'Caroline.' He whispered her name.

'Yes my dear. I'm here.'

He turned to look at her through the blur of unshed tears. Black had never been her colour. It made her face look white and drawn. She had cried for days, but today, the day of the funeral, she was calm. White and drawn, but strong and calm. It seemed everyone had been able to shed tears for Beth - except him. His beautiful eldest daughter, born to his first wife, had matured into a beautiful young lady in her teenage years but the sickness had taken her suddenly and unexpectedly. One day she'd been playing happily with her two sisters and young step-brother and eight weeks later she was being buried in the dark dank earth.

'Where is God in all this Caroline? Where is He? Does He even care?' His voice sounded hard and bitter. The bleak brown fields and lifeless trees seemed to stand by in silent condemnation at his accusation.

Caroline gently rubbed his shoulder but didn't say anything.

'Mummy, are we going home yet?' William tugged at Caroline's sleeve.

79

'Yes William. In one moment.' She took his other hand. 'These are the times we hold on in faith Robert. We trust God is with us even though our pain makes us feel deserted. He is with dear Beth now. I know He is! If I doubted that for one moment I could not go on, but Jesus has healed her sickness and she is out of pain.' She patted his arm. 'Come along Robert. Our children are cold. Let's take them home. There are some lovely letters from our friends and from the shop. Their prayers will uphold us.' She sounded so sure, so hopeful, that even in the midst of his grief, Robert Middleton dared to reach out to grasp that ray of hope. Caroline was right. He would let the prayers of his friends, family, the trustees, staff and customers of The Bible & Tract Depot, uphold him in this terrible time.

******

Business was flourishing at the beginning of the century for the Bible & Tract Depot, but then this was a time when the western world as a whole was being swept along by an economic boom and technical advancement. Newcastle upon Tyne had developed into a regional shopping centre and Northumberland Street, one of its main shopping areas, attracted custom from all over the north-east and beyond. Crowds thronged Fenwick's department store and if they were unable to find what they wanted, took the short walk to the Bainbridge Shop, on Market Street.

One of the advantages of shopping at Bainbridge's, was you could visit the new elaborately decorated "Ladies Tea Room," with its arcaded panelling and ornamental palisades, but it wasn't just tea they served. Coffee was now a growing commodity and the coffee for Bainbridges Ladies Tea Room, provided by Mr Pumphrey, ensured that business for Mr Pumphrey, Thomas Bainbridge and his brother, Alderman George Bainbridge, a recent Trustee to The Bible & Tract Depot, flourished.

Electric tramways now ran through the city centre, replacing the old horse-drawn trams, although the hackney carriages, standing at St. Nicholas Square, still did a roaring trade. Mosley Street, became the first streets to replace the old gas lamps with the new electric lamps.

International trade increased rapidly with the development of more sophisticated harbour facilities. Staiths were erected to ship the millions of tons of coal from the River Tyne. This Victorian expansion of industry and commerce meant more money in the wage earners pocket and what did people want to spend this extra money on? Entertainment! Motion pictures were now the entertainment of the future and Newcastle upon Tyne authorities were all set to accommodate the public demand for cinemas. Many Christians however, were greatly upset by what they saw as a new evil in their midst.

Much to the Temperance Movement's delight, horse racing had been transferred to Gosforth Park and they were now able to hold their Temperance Festival on the Town Moor during the "Race Week" in June, as a counter attraction. This proved to be an enormous success. Families thronged to watch the military competitions and to enjoy the travelling fairs and children's games.

Robert Middleton and Caroline usually enjoyed taking their children to the Temperance Festival on the Town Moor, but with the loss of Robert's eldest daughter, Beth, this years outing was filled with deep sadness. He had thought serving in a Christian book shop would have enabled him to come to terms with his loss, but it didn't. In fact, as the year progressed, he found himself more and more angry with God and began harbouring doubts over the existence of a supposed God of love who could allow such a dreadful thing to happen. Not that he would dare share these wicked thoughts with anyone. He was torn with guilt even admitting them to himself! He found it easier to cope by throwing himself wholeheartedly into the business and the trustees were eternally grateful to him for that. None of them realising this was his means of escaping the deep grief he was unable to shed.

Robert Middleton had often felt that there were two weak links in The Bible & Tract Depot. The first was that they had to depend largely on customers being able to find the premises. Now, having employed John Stephenson as colporteur, the Word of God was being carried from door-to-door, endeavouring to place in the hands of the working class, books of a reliable character. This was their attempt to counteract the trashy literature being circulated so freely in the north-east.

The second weak link was the condition of the premises. They'd been forced to concrete under the joists last year due to a plague of rats which had sent Miss Gibson into hysterics. Then they had had to fit a gas jet in the water closet to prevent the pipes from bursting in frosty weather. Mr Pumphrey had brought in pots of ivy which had been placed in front of the building to make it look nice, yet despite the costly improvements, Mr

81

Lamb failed to give any sort of guarantee beyond the terms of their current lease. The Trustees were most displeased! They therefore decided, after considerable discussion, searching and enquiries, to take a step of faith and proceed with the purchase of premises owned by a Mr Foster. These were at No. 14, Pilgrim Street. In recent years the Corporation had seen fit to change the door numbers making No.14, higher up the street than one would imagine. In fact, as it was only a few yards from busy Northumberland Street, the trustees felt this would be a most agreeable move!.

The building itself needed a lot of work done to it. It had a good basement but at the moment it was unusable. The walls were strong but the staircase would have to be reconstructed between two of the storeys. Two floors would have to be remade at different levels, new doors and partitions would have to be fixed, walls plastered, papered and painted and a heating system provided. It had been agreed to try to complete the work within the next year and they were well on their way to meeting that target.

Robert Middleton looked forward to the move with mixed feelings. He had always been of the opinion that the Trustees had been throwing good money into bad property which they were only leasing anyway, and although he didn't relish the upheaval of moving, the thought of actually purchasing premises more suitable for their business, appealed to him. His work load had increased as he was responsible for organising builders to attend to the necessary alterations.

This came at a time when there was a change in policy in The Bible & Tract Depot. Sunday School Teachers were now able to select their stock from the shop rather than from catalogues, which meant Robert Middleton was forced to fit in extra trips to London for stock. This also had the effect of increasing the workload for the staff who were already busy stocktaking in preparation for the forthcoming move.

'I dunno! All this extra work is killing me!' Jane Gibson grumbled, as she watered Mr Pumphrey's pots of ivy. 'And I've got me ma poorly so I've to do the washin' and cookin' when I gets meself home!' Her usual cheerful face was sombre despite the bright August sunshine streaming in through the window. 'I divvint dare take any more time off work or I'll be in trouble.'

'What does your father say?' Henrietta Harris asked. There'd been a succession of shop girls after Caroline, so Henry Harris had brought in his

82

sixteen-year old daughter to be trained. A thin, quiet, mousy girl, prone to moods of depression and headaches.

Jane shrugged. 'Divvint talk about me da! He, and me brother, Tom think I should give up work to mind me ma and what can I do? Me ma's right sick! When I tried telling them I helped out as shop girl cos I could now read and write they just laughed and said a girl's place is in the home.' She sighed. 'I know they've brought in Mary Bean to help do me deliveries while me ma's bad, but I'm having to think seriously about leaving the shop altogether.'

Henrietta's eyes opened wide. 'Oh Jane! You can't do that!' She'd become dependant this brash friendly girl who talked non-stop and the very idea of having to work with someone else scared her.

Jane sniffed and wiped her nose across her sleeve. 'Aye! Well I might have to if me da has his way. Although mind you, I divint want to. In fact I quite fancy moving into these new premises. Your da..er Mr Harris says they've even got a netty inside the house instead of in the yard. I could fancy that! Hey watch it! Here's Mr Bainbridge.'

Thomas Bainbridge hurried into the shop followed closely by his youngest two sons, Lindsay and Wilfred, now handsome young men in their late teens. All three men were most alarmed to see their shop girl, Henrietta Harris, turn white at the sight of them. She gripped the side of the counter, swayed uncertainly then fled into the back. Jane Gibson's jaw dropped opened in surprise as Mr Harris bustled forward to greet them, his thin sharp features flushed with embarrassment.

'I do apologise for Miss Harris, Mr Bainbridge, sirs.' He stuttered wringing his hands anxiously. 'She is of a...a slight nervous disposition. Takes after her mother's side of the family. I had hoped a few weeks meeting good upstanding Christian customers would rectify the matter, however........'

Thomas Bainbridge broke into what was obviously going to be a long drawn out apology. 'Not to worry Mr Harris. I'm sure that given time, Miss Harris will get used to us. I came to see Mr Middleton. Is he around?'

'Yes sir. In the office upstairs.'

Thomas turned to his sons. 'I won't be long boys. Amuse yourselves for ten minutes will you?'

Thomas Bainbridge took the stairs two at a time and arrived at the top panting. Giving a sharp rap on the office door he didn't wait for a reply but walked in. The white, gaunt face of his manager, whom he hadn't seen for some weeks, looked up from the desk where he was working. Thomas stood for a moment, taken aback by his appearance.

'You do not look at all well Mr Middleton.' he said gently. 'I hope you have not been overworking?'

Robert stood up and ignoring the question indicated the chair opposite him. Thomas shook his head. 'No, I won't sit down. I have a meeting with the heads of department at Bainbridges in half an hour. I just called in to see if the Newcastle Colporteurs had replied to our letter.'

The Bible and Tract Depot had written to the Newcastle Colporteurs, complaining that their staff were securing orders for themselves from Sunday School teachers, ministers and others who traded with the Bible and Tract Depot, for books far below cost price.

Robert cleared his throat and his face twisted into an angry scowl. 'Not a word sir! Not a word! And this is not the first time it has happened!'

Thomas raised his eyebrows at the unexpected venom in his tone.

Robert coughed, a little embarrassed and shuffled a few papers on his desk. 'We have stressed once before that we believe, whenever possible, the generous grant we give Newcastle Colporteurs each year ought to be spent here, at our depot. We also made a point of telling them that the Newcastle Sunday School Union and the Newcastle Bible Society, both of whom also receive substantial grants from us, continue to generously help and advance our work. Yet they continue to ignore us!' Robert's voice shook with emotion. 'Hopefully we will receive a reply within the next two weeks, after they have had time to consider our wishes.'

Thomas nodded. 'Good, good.' He hesitated. 'Mr Middleton. I wonder if we have been working you too hard. Perhaps you would consider taking a few days leave.'

Robert looked at the older man aghast. 'With all due respect sir,' he replied stiffly, 'I have never had a day's absence from this shop in all the years I have worked here. Other than my annual leave and the.....the....day of...the loss of my ...daughter......' Robert's voice trailed off into silence as emotion got the better of him.

Mr. Middleton's distress did not go unnoticed by Thomas Bainbridge. He raised his hand. 'Your point is taken Mr Middleton. However I would like you to reconsider. You sound....tired and you are far too valuable an employee to lose through ill health.' He glanced at his pocket watch as he saw Robert Middleton was about to embark upon another argument. 'Now, I really must go.' He turned at the door with the intention of enquiring over the strange behaviour of Henrietta Harris, but changed his mind. Robert Middleton had enough on his plate at the moment. Instead he asked, 'How is the new delivery girl settling in?'

'Miss Bean? She's very slow and it's difficult to get a word out of her but I think she's settling down all right sir.'

Thomas smiled. 'No doubt Miss Gibson's tongue makes up for Miss Bean's silences. Is Miss Gibson still having to take time off work?'

Robert didn't smile. 'Unfortunately yes, and it may be she is forced to leave us altogether to care for her sick mother.' His brow creased with a worried frown. 'We are also losing Mrs Richie, our cleaner who has found employment elsewhere. All this in the middle of moving. It is most inconvenient.'

Thomas was concerned to see his manager's hands shake as they rested on the desk but all he said was, 'Let me know how things progress Mr Middleton will you?' Robert Middleton wouldn't take kindly to any interference in his work.

'Yes sir.'

Thomas closed the door thoughtfully and hurried downstairs. He caught a glimpse of Henrietta Harris, peering nervously around the back door and Jane Gibson's vague worried face as she stood watering plants. Henry Harris was trying to calm down an irate customer who was insisting he'd been given the wrong change and the new delivery girl, Miss Bean, was gazing adoringly at his younger son, Wilfred. The place was like a mad house this morning! A mad house!

'Lindsay! Wilfred! Time to go!' He hadn't meant to snap as he marched out of the shop and that he had done so caused raised eyebrows from both boys as they obediently followed their father out of the shop and into Pilgrim Street. Something had upset him this morning.

Thomas glanced at his watch. 'I have an....an errand to attend to boys.'

Wilfred glanced at his watch. 'You have a meeting at Bainbridge's in fifteen minutes father.'

'I know! I know! Ask your Uncle George to start without me if I'm late.'

The brothers glanced at each other. Their father was always very punctual for meetings. This must be a very important errand.

85

'All right father. We'll see you later.'

Thomas just grunted and raised his hand in a farewell gesture. He needed time to clear his head and think and a brisk walk to the top of Northumberland Street, towards the Haymarket, should help him get his thoughts in order.

He passed the new Northern Goldsmiths. Their expensive and elegant jewellery sparkled in the bright August sunshine but Thomas didn't notice. His mind was elsewhere. He crossed over Blackett Street into Northumberland Street. A young barrow boy, his barrow laden with baskets of bread shouted, 'Watch it mister!' but he just side-stepped the barrow and kept walking. He passed his rival, Fenwick's. Normally he would have taken great interest in what the elegant ladies who graced the department store were buying, but not today.

He seemed to reach the top of Northumberland Street in no time and found himself standing outside St. Thomas Church in the Haymarket. Travellers on their way from the city to the Town Moor couldn't fail to be reminded of God as they passed this building. It's magnificent spire stood proudly overlooking the city and its doors were always open. Thomas decided he needed more time to think so he went inside.

It was very quiet inside the church. Rays of sunshine streamed through the stained glass windows leaving rainbows of colour around the church. He sat down on one of the hard wooden pews and after gazing at the beautiful altar before him for a while, bowed his head in prayer.

'Oh Lord.' His whisper was barely audible even to himself but it seemed to echo around the rafters of the building. 'Thou knowest the troubles of these Godly people whom we have employed to serve you in Your Bible and Tract Depot. They appear to be a troubled bunch and some inner instinct tells me this isn't due entirely to the moving of premises.' Thomas lent forward, resting on the pew in front of him. 'Lord, I hear the untold grief in Mr Robert Middleton for his daughter and his staffing problems. I see the worry of Miss Jane Gibson for her mother, the overworked Mr Henry Harris and his concerns over his depressive and most odd daughter.' Thomas's voice shook just a little. 'Forgive us Father. For in the growth and development of our own businesses, perhaps we......no! Perhaps I as a trustee was not aware of the problems they were carrying. Problems made even greater by the pressure of moving to No. 14, Pilgrim Street.' A deep pang of compassion stirred inside him as the image of Robert Middleton's white, gaunt face flashed across his mind. He like the man. Friendly, loyal and sincere. His prayers moved on to Miss Jane Gibson, the young delivery girl who had worked so hard to learn to read and write and acquire the position of shop girl, only to have it snatched away from her because she was needed at home to nurse her mother. His thoughts then turned to Mr Harris, who seemed obsessed with checking the till at least twice a day in case any more money went missing. It never had, but Mr Harris lived in fear of it happening again. Then there was Henrietta Harris. What caused an apparently healthy young girl to suffer fits of depression and attacks of panic? There was something not quite right with her. And Miss Bean? Well he didn't really know anything about the young lady. She'd only been employed a few weeks but she had obviously taken a fancy to his son, Wilfred.

When Thomas Bainbridge had finished praying he sat very still. He was totally oblivious to the lady arranging flowers on the altar or passers-by taking a few minutes away from shopping in the heat to pray in the cool and quiet sanctuary of St. Thomas Church. Despite Thomas's busy life he knew that when he set time aside for God like this, God had a way of speaking direction and inspiration into the things that troubled him. He was unaware how long he'd sat in the church until a door slamming somewhere behind him brought him out of his meditating. He glanced at his pocket watch. No point going to the meeting at Bainbridge's now. It would be over. As Thomas rose to his feet he didn't feel distressed by this. Quite the opposite. He knew without any shadow of doubt that time spent with God was never wasted.

******

'Ah! Miss Gibson. A word with you if you have a moment.' Henry Harris peered over his spectacles to where a pasty faced Jane Gibson stood wrapping books in brown paper ready for delivery to one of their customers. 'Henrietta. Could you serve the customers while I speak with Miss Gibson please.'

Henrietta shivered. She hated serving customers! She hated people! She hated the job! She hated.....! She didn't know what she hated, she just knew she couldn't seem to rid herself of this dark depression that continually washed over her. When it came, all she wanted to do was lie down and sleep but all she ever heard was, 'Oh, pull yourself together Henrietta!'

'Yes sir.' she murmured. Even though Henry Harris was her father, etiquette demanded she call him "Mr", or "Sir", like the rest of the staff.

'Miss Gibson,' Mr Harris said when they were at the back of the shop. 'The trustees have asked me to have a word with you.'

Jane Gibson felt the nerves in her stomach tighten. This was it! They were going to ask her to leave because she'd had so much time off work caring for her mother.

'Yes sir.' She lifted her chin. She wouldn't cry! She just wouldn't!

'It has been brought to the notice of the Trustees that you are prevented from attending to your usual duties by your mother's serious illness.'

Jane nodded numbly. 'I'm sorry Mr Harris sir. I know it's inconvenient, especially with all the extra work at the moment, but me ma's right sick and I'm up every night to 'er, then there's the washing and.....'

'Yes. Quite! Quite! Miss Gibson. The Trustees have noted your er... predicament and have suggested I offer you time off work to attend to your mother and er... the home. You will be paid two shillings a week to keep your job open and we will ask Miss Bean to work extra hours. Would this arrangement help your situation at all?'

Jane Gibson stared at the little man with her mouth wide open. 'Help! It would be bloo...., it would be of great help Mr Harris sir,' she gulped. It seemed inconceivable that important men like Mr Thomas Bainbridge, Alderman George Bainbridge, Mr Pumphrey, Mr David Richardson, Mr Scott, Mr Watson and all the other influential business men in the city, would even notice the predicament of a person such as herself. 'Would you thank them for me sir. It is most generous.'

'Yes, of course. And if you should find you could spare the odd half day, especially at the moment with so much to do, we would be most grateful Miss Gibson. Miss Bean is a little slow and uncertain and Henrietta is....yes well, we would be most grateful.' He glanced over Jane Gibson's shoulder towards the counter and was alarmed to see a small queue of customers and the counter unattended. 'Miss Gibson, I think we better attend to our work, at once!'

There was a note of alarm in his voice that prompted Jane to follow him quickly across the shop floor. Curled up underneath the counter, out of sight of the customers, was Henrietta, her knees to her chin, her face white and terrified, her body shaking.

Henry Harris's face turned into a mask of fury. 'Henrietta! Pull yourself together girl!'

But Jane Gibson knelt down beside the terrified girl and wrapped her arms around her.

'Hush now.' she whispered in her ear. 'Hush. Let's you and me go out the back eh?' Grabbing her woollen shawl from the peg and wrapping it around Henrietta's shaking shoulders she helped the girl to stand up. Henry Harris, turned to the customers stuttering his apologies while Jane Gibson almost carried Henrietta's limp body across the shop floor and out of the back door.

'Take lots of deep breaths, get your cheeks pink again.' she ordered propping the girl up against the yard wall. Henrietta followed instructions without a word, her eyes were glazed and stared beyond Jane to the roofs of the houses opposite. Jane didn't speak but continued to hold the young girl's hand as she watched the colour slowly return to her cheeks.

Eventually she asked, 'What happened Henrietta?'

Henrietta didn't reply at first but continued to stare ahead of her. 'I think....I think there's something.... wrong with ... with me.' she whispered in a low voice and one small tear rolled down her face. Jane couldn't think of a suitable reply so she just remained silent, gently stroking her hand. 'My parents keep telling me to pull myself together.' Henrietta continued, still in the same low voice. 'I try. I really do, but I can't seem to help this...this... One minute I'm all right, then suddenly I'll panic or start crying for no apparent reason. I'm tired all the time. I've no energy...' Her voice trailed off.

'Have you been to see a doctor?'

Henrietta shook her head. 'They just say there's no need.' Jane assumed by 'they' she meant her parents. 'They say all I have to do is pull myself together. I try! I really do but I feel everyone is against me. No-one seems to understand.'

Tears were rolling profusely down her cheeks by now and Jane was tempted to say, 'Come on! Cheer up!' but somehow it seemed the wrong thing to say. Henrietta had been listening to this for years and it hadn't helped her any. She was at a loss to know what to suggest so she just let Henrietta cry.

Eventually Jane said, 'I have an idea.'

Henrietta wiped her tear-stained face and for the first time looked directly at Jane. 'What?'

'You said nobody seems to understand. Well, you can come around to my place on Sunday afternoon and try to help me understand if you like?'

Henrietta looked at her suspiciously. 'But why would you want to?'

Jane shrugged. 'We're friends aren't we?'

'What about your mother?'

'What about her? Me da and me brother, Tom can watch her while you and me go for a walk. I'll bake a cake for our tea eh?'

Henrietta hesitated. 'Isn't that too much trouble......?'

'No it isn't. You'll be doing me a favour.'

'Will I?'

'Course you will. If I'm gonna be at home all week nursing her I'll need a break and some proper company. Not just me da and our Tom. Are you comin' then?'

A hesitant smile softened the contours of Henrietta's mouth and Jane couldn't help but think what a pretty face she would have if she smiled more often. She almost told her so but thought better of it. She'd made progress if she could get Henrietta Harris to smile. Best leave it at that.

'Yes. That would be lovely. Thank you.'

Jane patted her hand. 'Howay then! We better get back or we'll have miserable Middleton barking at us.'

******

It was a case of all hands on deck during the move to No. 14, Pilgrim Street. The only major problem was, there were not enough hands. Henrietta Harris spent most of the time complaining of a severe headache and having to sit down, totally unable to cope with all the comings and goings. Jane Gibson's mother had taken a turn for the worse and according to her brother Tom, who called in at the shop on his way to work, Jane probably wouldn't be back for the rest of the week. Mrs Richie, the cleaner, was moving her belongings out of the rooms upstairs to her new place of employment and the horse and cart that stood at the door piled high with furniture only seemed to add to the congestion around the shop.

'I'm sure it can't have been as chaotic moving into this place as it is moving out!' Lindsay Bainbridge grumbled staggering across the shop floor, his arms full of books.

John Stephenson grinned, his thoughts flashing back over the years to his sister Mary Jane and Hannah Grigs and their move into No. 17, Pilgrim Street..

'Believe me it was! Just as chaotic.'

John Stephenson, Wilfred and Lindsay Bainbridge and Robert Middleton had been left doing most of the heavy work of carrying books, shelving and furniture from the present premises to the new shop. Ruth Grigs and Mary Bean were rolling linoleum and Henry Harris was in a flap, rushing from shop to shop. But somehow, by the end of the day, the staff of The Bible & Tract Depot and their helpers had moved into their own beautifully-decorated premises, their only disappointment being that they still had to use gas lamps instead of electric lights.

At half-past seven that evening, Robert Middleton left Mr Harris to lock the doors of No. 14, while he returned to No.17, Pilgrim Street to make sure they had left the premises clean and tidy. Most of the shops in the city had closed for the evening and other than a few window shoppers enjoying the warm summer evening and the occasional tramcar and hackney carriage clattering up Pilgrim Street, the town was quiet.

As Robert Middleton entered the premises of No.17, Pilgrim Street and closed the door behind him he was filled with a deep sense of sadness. He made his way slowly up the stairs to the top floor of the building, into the two rooms that had once been occupied by Ted and Annie Stephenson and their two children, John and Mary Jane. These rooms had recently been rented out as offices and meeting rooms to the North of England Temperance League, until it required more office accommodation than The Bible & Tract Depot had been able to give. Robert looked out of the window. There was a magnificent view up and down Pilgrim Street. Despite the fact that many of the houses in Northumberland Street and Pilgrim Street had been converted into shops and electricity was spreading rapidly throughout the city, the courts and alleys at the back of these streets were still inhabited by people whose living conditions had barely improved in the last 50 years. From his vantage point at the top of the house however, none of this could be seen. Just the tramcars rattling up the road, the Police Station and Courts, where The Bible and Tract had first set up the business, and various houses and shops that had been built and developed with the city. Robert closed the door on what had been Annie's rooms, but was still left with his deep sense of sadness.

91

He entered Elisabeth Smith's and latterly Mrs Richie's two rooms, although in his mind it would always remain "Miss Smith's place". His feet echoed across the wooden floorboards as he walked across the room. A dilapidated black kitchen range which had seen better days, stood in the corner. This had been transferred from Mr Ephraim Lister's kitchen when the municipal authorities had knocked down the very first Depot. He ran his hand thoughtfully along the top of the range and he remembered that Miss Smith had often stood by this range.

'Come in dear boy! Come in!' she'd barked at him and as a young manager of twenty-five, they'd talk business during the half-hour he gave himself for his mid-day break. Everything he'd needed to know had been at Miss Smith's fingertips. Dear Miss Smith. Dear, dear.... Miss Smith.....For no accountable reason tears sprang into his eyes. Perhaps it was standing so alone in these empty rooms that had at one time felt so homely to him. Perhaps it was a reminder of the emptiness that death.......... Robert stifled a sob and turning abruptly on his heel hurried out of "Elisabeth Smith's place". He glanced briefly into the office where he had spent many hours and the community room which had been let to a succession of organisations. Then he hurried downstairs into the shop, quite annoyed with himself. It was ridiculous getting sentimental over a shop!

The bare walls, streaked with dirt where the shelves had been, closed in on him. The grate where endless delivery girls and shop girls had kept cheerful fires blazing on cold winters days, stood empty, lifeless. This was where he had met Caroline for the first time. He rested his arms on the narrow mantelpiece and shivered as the emptiness that had been gnawing at him all day seemed to merge with the emptiness he had experienced since the death of his daughter.

Many friends had told him that he should be over his period of mourning by now but he had never been able to accept the reality of Beth's death in the first place. He had remained locked in shock and denial, unable to cope with the pain confronting him. But in reflecting over the life of The Bible & Tract Depot, the people who had worked there over the years, their joys and their sorrows, had triggered off in Robert the need to respond to his own loss.

'Beth.' It was hardly a whisper but it was the first time he had spoken her name since the day she died. 'Oh Beth! My....my Beth!' With his head resting on the back of his hands, his shoulders shook as he gave vent to his long-buried grief which rose to the surface. Tears streamed down both cheeks and dripped into the firegrate.

He had no idea how long he was there. Time seemed to stand still as wave upon wave of grief washed over him threatening to drown him. His body ached with weeping but eventually he reached a point when there were no more tears left to shed, not that night anyway. Slowly he pushed himself away from the mantelpiece and searched for his handkerchief to mop his tear-stained face. Through watery eyes he looked out towards Pilgrim Street. It was a familiar scene. He had stood in this place on many occasions staring out of this same window, reflecting on business problems or members of his staff but tonight it was different. The business was the same, the problems would be the same and so would the members of staff but they would all be reflected upon from a different setting.

'Yea though I walk through the valley of the shadow of death
I will fear no evil. For thou art with me.'

Just then a nearby street lamp flared into life and its light flickered through the window and illuminated the far side of the room. It seemed to Robert that it had also filtered into the darkest reaches of his soul chasing away the shadows of fear as, for the first time since her death, he was able to recall his daughter's face; her smile, her laughter and her joy. There was light at the end of the endless dark tunnel he had been walking through. He had known there must be but now! Now he sensed it. Now he sensed........God! He stood quietly and unemotionally drinking in the first waves of healing.

It seemed like a long time he stood in that place of healing. Eventually he glanced at his pocket watch. It was late. Caroline would be concerned about him. Poor Caroline. He'd neglected her shamefully over the past few months. He dabbed his eyes, straightened his jacket, lifted his head and as Robert Middleton locked the door of No.17, Pilgrim Street for the last time, he had a vivid sense of new beginnings.

1912

In time Wilfrid Bainbridge had felt a strong sense of duty to follow his father Thomas, into the family firm of Bainbridge & Co. Of Thomas' four sons Wilfrid was most like his father in character and interests. However, his brother Lindsay, who was two years older, had chosen a career in engineering and had served an apprenticeship with Wallsend Shipyards. Thomas had been annoyed by Lindsay's decision not to join the family firm and, inevitably, there were arguments between them.

'Why can't you join Wilfred and I at the store, Lindsay?'

Lindsay was adamant. 'How many more times do we have to have this conversation father? I want to be involved in shipbuilding!'

'All right! Shipbuilding. Then why do you spend so much time playing with...with toy aeroplanes of all things!'

'They are not toys, father. They are model aeroplanes and I fly them because I'm interested in the aerodynamics of flight. Why should that annoy you?'

Although Lindsay and his father failed to agree over his choice of career, Lindsay admired his father and was dreadfully upset when the good Lord saw fit to take his father in 1912.

Thomas and Kate had been entertaining a big family shooting party at Eshott Hall when the first twinges occurred. On consulting his doctor Thomas was diagnosed with appendicitis and he was advised to have an immediate operation.

Kate, naturally anxious, was reassured by the doctor who said 'Our dear King Edward had his appendix successfully removed just a few years ago, This operation is now almost common practice. Nothing to worry about. Nothing at all!'

A few days later after the operation, complications set in and Thomas Bainbridge died leaving a devastated Kate and family to mourn him.

The funeral, held in Jesmond Methodist Church, was attended by hundreds of mourners as people from all walks of life came to pay their last respects to this well-loved man.

War: 1914-18

Kate hadn't wanted her two youngest sons to go to war, not so soon after Tom's death, but they both felt called into the struggle. There really was no need for Wilfrid, in particular, to volunteer as he was carrying the responsibility of a great business on his shoulders. Unlike many young men who were caught up in the false glamour and adventure of it all, war offered no attraction for Wilfred. He saw it for what it was. Anyway, he told himself, there really wasn't any other option. Austria's mobilisation against Serbia had begun a series of events which had eventually plunged Europe into a war that was taking thousands of lives, among them his brother Lindsay! Dear Lindsay! A Lieutenant in the 5th Northumberland Fusiliers, he had been killed in action in Belgium a few days after his arrival in 1915 at the age of thirty-three.

******

The shop bell tinkled as Wilfrid opened the door of The Bible & Tract Depot and Mr Harris looked up.

'Nice to see you again Mr Wilfred, sir!' He said, casting an uneasy eye over Wilfrid's uniform. 'I gather you are on leave from France?'

'Yes, I am Mr Harris.'

'Terrible thing war sir! Terrible thing! You must have seen some awful sights.'

Wilfred's face momentarily darkened. 'I have indeed Mr Harris but I have also been privileged to witness acts of great courage and bravery in the face of the enemy.'

'No doubt sir.' Mr Harris agreed soberly. 'No doubt.' Although a pacifist, he had great admiration for the commitment and bravery of the young men who were being sent to war.

'I'm actually here to collect the books my mother ordered.' Wilfred said.

'Ah yes.' He searched among the pile of books standing on the corner of the counter.

'How long are you expecting to be with us Mr Wilfred?'

'Only a few days Mr Harris.' He saw little Mary Bean peering at him admiringly from behind the small stand of books in the centre of the shop and smiled across at her. Her round face turned red with embarrassment. There was a sudden loud ringing as the telephone on the counter burst into life and Wilfred noted with some amusement the way the staff jumped at the unexpected sound. Obviously they hadn't quite come to terms with this modern piece of equipment. Mr Harris cautiously picked up the ear piece.

'Hello!' he shouted down the mouth piece. 'This is The Bible & Tract Depot!'

95

There was a moments silence while the person at the other end spoke. Then, 'Yes.' (pause) 'Yes.' (pause) Yes.' (pause) 'Good-bye.'

'Our new telephone.' Mr Harris explained, as if explanations were necessary. 'There's an extension to the Sunday School Union Office upstairs and we keep a full account of every message sent out and then divide the costs between us.'

'Good idea.' Wilfred said, There was a moments silence before he politely asked, 'And how is your daughter Mr Harris?' He glanced around the shop but there was no sign of her. 'She was not feeling well during my last visit and being in France has left me behind with news.'

Henry Harris dropped his eyes and looked decidedly uncomfortable. 'Ahem! She er.....er is unfortunately quite poorly sir.'

'I'm sorry to hear that Mr Harris. Please give her my kindest regards for a speedy recovery won't you?'

'I will indeed sir. Thank you for your er...concern.'

It was only when he returned home to see his mother that he was brought up-to-date with more news.

'Oh my dear!' exclaimed Kate. 'I should have warned you. Poor Henrietta Harris became most disturbed in her mind. But sit down Wilfred. I'll arrange for afternoon tea to be brought to us.' She rang the bell and a few minutes later a tray of tea, sandwiches and cake was brought into the library for them.

Wilfred sat back in the chair and allowed the tensions of war to drain out of him as he absorbed the magnificent views across the open fields through the large windows of Eshott Hall. He loved this place. His father had built several extensions to the Hall so that his children would always feel there was room for them and their friends to stay, but the library was Wilfred's favourite.

He and Kate had caught up on family news particularly the development of the Bainbridge shop which now occupied the whole length of Market Street. His eldest brother Jack was taking on the upkeep of Eshott Hall. He was also interested on how the war was affecting the country before eventually coming round to Henrietta Harris.

'It seems,' said Kate pouring him another cup of tea, 'That Miss Harris was becoming stranger by the day. Miss Jane Gibson was very good for her, invited her for tea and encouraged her to talk but there was something not quite right. Miss Harris was of a nervous disposition and took to crying for the slightest reason.' Kate handed Wilfred his cup and saucer and he helped himself to a sandwich. 'Such a worry for her dear parents and of course for Mr Harris having to reprimand her for her abnormal behaviour at the shop. It was beginning to cause problems.'

'What happened?'

Kate sat back comfortably in her chair. 'Crying in front of customers, deep depressions, forgetting things, disappearing into the basement to be alone. Eventually her dear parents sought the advice of a doctor and much to their distress he suggested Miss Harris be sent to a sanatorium.' Kate shook her head. 'So very sad. I gather the Trustees have granted her leave of absence and a small sum to tide her over and Mr Middleton has written on their behalf expressing their sympathy and best wishes for a complete recovery.' Kate took a sip of tea. 'I understand she's only expected to be in for three months but unfortunately, even in today's advanced world of medicine, there is still a degree of shame attached to mental illness. Poor Miss Harris. The Lord knows what those places are like!' She lifted the plate of cakes. 'Try a piece of sandwich cake Wilfred dear?'

'Yes. Poor Miss Harris.' He reached forward and took a slice of cake.

'The only good thing to have come out of the whole sorry episode is the gratuity of giving two guineas to Miss Bean for all the extra work she had to do with Miss Harris being absent. Mr Harris trained her to be a shop girl. My goodness! You'd think she'd been given the crown jewels she was so delighted! Oh yes, and the other thing you missed was Mr Robert Middleton celebrating twenty-five years as manager and secretary of The Bible & Tract Depot.'

Wilfred smiled. It was quite amazing how his mother could jump from one subject to another.

Kate chuckled. 'You should have seen Mr Middleton's face when the trustees presented him with a gratuity of fifteen guineas and an instruction to take an extra weeks holiday.'

Kate bit neatly into a piece of sandwich cake and silence descended upon the library at Eshott Hall while she ate.

Eventually she said, 'You know Wilfred, for a time I thought that dear man, Mr Middleton I mean, would never recover from the death of his daughter. He was so pale and drawn and seemed to be getting thinner at the passing of each week, but since the shop moved into No.14 Pilgrim Street, he seems to have recovered some of his old enthusiasm for life. I called around to see Mrs Caroline Middleton the other day. Their eldest boy, William is growing fast. Which reminds me Wilfred. I have a gift for you.'

Kate placed her cup on the tray and reached for the parcel of books Wilfred had brought from the shop. Unwrapping the brown paper she brought out a small black Bible. 'I thought a small copy of the Bible would fit more easily into one of your uniform pockets Wilfred dear,' she said handing it to him with a smile.

He held the small leather book in his hand. 'It's beautiful.' He reached over and taking her hand in his, kissed her fingers. 'Thank you mother dear.'

1916

Wilfrid was momentarily blinded by a searing pain as the bullet knocked him backwards. He lay spread-eagled in the trench, his head tilted forward at an awkward angle, watching the red blood spreading across the front of his tunic. He had always expected that it would happen. Somehow he had always known that the fields of France would be his final resting place but he hadn't expected it would happen quite so soon. One of his comrades drop to his knees by his side.

'Wilf! Oh my God Wilfred! Orderly! *Orderly!*' A shell burst less than six feet away and he heard himself let out a piercing scream as his comrade fell across him, jarring his whole body with pain. Thankfully he welcomed the dark wave of unconsciousness that engulfed him.

It was pain that brought him back into the world again. Into a cold grey world in France, where there was nothing but rain and confusion and more rain. Small units of men who had been engaged in formless savage attacks now wandered around in a daze, unsure which way they should be advancing, their faces cowed and haunted, their helmets and rifles discarded. Young boys isolated from their companions scrambled through a gap in the barbed wire, weeping from the sight of dead and wounded bodies they were leaving behind in No Man's Land. Older veterans of war who had dug in hard in the trenches, huddled together with the expressionless eyes of men who had been driven to edge and then forced over. German artillery fire which had been spasmodic all day rattled close by. As Lieutenant Adjutant in the 6th Northumberland Fusiliers, Wilfred felt he ought to be there with them, giving orders, reassuring. Even in his wounded state his heart bled for these men. His eyes shifted towards the broad back of the orderly.

'Just be still sir. We'll soon have you seen to.' The voice came from behind him. He was on a stretcher. They were carrying him towards the first aid post, slithering and sliding in the mud. There was the sound of an explosion. The stretcher wobbled as the orderlies ducked and earth and rocks showered down upon them. Someone began screaming. It was a cry of sheer desolation. Wilfred Bainbridge closed his eyes. He was in hell! *HELL*! Death itself held no terrors for him but the prospect of the pain he would have to endure before he reached that place was daunting. He kept his eyes closed.It was easier that way. He had already lost too many of his men. Only a small group had returned earlier that morning with stories of wandering through deserted trenches at night, knee deep in water. They had heard the whine of the shells but in the dark and confusion only a few of them had made it to the shelter.

The smell of dank, burnt woodland told him the stretcher squad were now out of firing range. The orderlies boots squelched in the sodden undergrowth, their long heavy overcoats, little enough protection from the ceaseless rain, caught on the briars and barbed wire.

It was easy to remember a time when there was no war. When the condition of Ireland dominated the newspapers, or the militancy of the suffragettes covered the front pages and there was only the threat of war in Europe, not the reality. That was the time before this God-forsaken place became a battlefield.

He felt himself being lifted up on to a table. Just the sheer effort of his body being jostled made him cry out. Then he heard someone say, 'My God! What a mess!' and somehow he knew they were referring to him. He opened his eyes to see a man he assumed to be the doctor standing over him, his bare arms and apron splattered in blood. He smiled down at him. 'Take it easy son.' he said. 'You're in the ADS.' (Advanced Dressing Station) and Wilfred was glad to slide into that place of unconsciousness once more, where carnage and desolation belonged to another world.

A change of environment with its different noises dragged Wilfred back into a pain-filled world. He opened his eyes. Cautiously he turned his head. He was in a hall of some sort and the long room where he lay had obviously been made into a hospital. Tightly packed rows of wounded soldiers lay staring at the ceiling, crying or moaning and there was the stench of unwashed human bodies.

'Hello. Glad to have you with us again,' a voice said quietly. The voice had a friendly face and the white cap on her head covered curly auburn hair. 'I'm a nurse. We've moved you to a base hospital. Would you like a drink?'

He could only mouth his confirmation as he seemed to have lost his voice. She lifted his head gently off the pillow so he could drink from the cup, but he could only take a few sips and he was glad when she gently lowered him on to the pillow again. She smiled down at him and the freckles on top of her nose wrinkled. 'I'll wash and clean you up when I've a minute.' she said softly, 'It'll make you more comfortable.' He tried to remember the last time he'd had a wash and gave up. He must look a wreck!

Then she walked away his eyes followed her. She reminded him of someone, a face from his past far from the horrors of war. He closed his eyes in an attempt to blot out the scene and made a conscious effort to focus his thoughts on the nurse. Then he remembered - it was young Jane Gibson from The Bible & Tract Depot. He smiled as his mind drifted back to the last time he had seen her.....

******

Nobody imagined that Jane would have joined the suffragettes, but she had. There she was at the end of a long line of suffragettes on an organised march down Northumberland Street. It was a gusty March day and she was attempting to keep her straw hat on with one hand and the board pinned to her front and rear steady. Wilfrid stopped outside Fenwick's Store to watch them and grinned broadly when he recognised her. She had seen him watching her and had flushed from embarrassment. Wilfird touched the brim of his hat courteously, still grinning but after a few minutes of keeping pace with them down Northumberland Street, she flounced away from her windswept friends and to his great amusement marched over to where he was standing.

'What do you think you're doing Wilfred Bainbridge?'

Still grinning, he'd pleaded his innocence. 'Nothing. What do you mean?'

'I'm on a good cause here!' she stormed. 'And I don't need the likes of you laughing at me.'

He smiled his most charming smile. 'Miss Gibson, I would never laugh at you.'

'Yes you would. It's the likes of you what keeps women second class citizens. We are seeking the right to vote, to have a say in what happens in our country and in our communities. We can do more than just stay at home nursing sick parents you know! We have the right to be educated, the right to.....!'

He raised his hands in mock surrender. 'All right! All right Miss Gibson! You've convinced me. I promise you I won't laugh any more.'

A gust of wind whipped around the corner from Blackett Street and Jane Gibson's board swung round banging him on the knee. 'Ouch!' He bent forward to rub his knee, while she nearly lost her straw hat. Hastily she grabbed at it and a smile tugged at the corner of her mouth. He stood up straight and they eyed each other with some amusement.

'Are you free for a cup of tea in the tearooms at Fenwick's, Miss Gibson.' he asked.

Her eyes opened wide. 'Are you serious?'

'Absolutely! You can tell me what you've been doing since you left The Bible & Tract Depot. The place isn't the same without you.'

'Now I know you're making fun of me.' she reproached.

He shook his head. 'Then let me made amends. Please have tea with me Miss Gibson.'

She pursed her lips. 'All right then.'

'Er...Without the board.'

She chuckled and between them they managed to extricate her from the sandwich board.

Wilfrid was always attracted to a pretty face and Jane Gibson, with her curly auburn hair, freckled face and lively conversation was no exception. Here was a young woman of principle who believed passionately in the rights of equal citizenship. Wilfred hadn't really given a lot of thought to the suffragette movement led by Emmiline Pankhurst and her fellow suffragettes, but found himself fascinated by the deep convictions of The Bible &Tract's former shop girl. Both her father and brother Tom, used to insist that her place was in the home caring for her mother, cooking their meals, washing their clothes and generally making life comfortable for them.

'Not that I minded looking after me ma.' Jane claimed, as she sipped her tea. 'But after she died I wanted to continue with me education and me dad and our Tom just laughed as if I had no right to an opinion, or a life of my own, come to that. Anyway I nagged and pleaded until eventually dad relented and allowed me to go back to night schools. Then the excitement started!. I met a group of young women like meself, who were sick of not having a say in things. I was greatly impressed, so.....' Jane shrugged her shoulders. 'Anyway, I joined them. Women have got a lot to offer this country and when we get the vote......'

'*If* you get the vote.' he corrected.

She looked him straight in the eye. He wasn't used to that. Women usually flickered their eyelashes at him in a flirtatious gesture. 'Haven't you heard of Emmeline Pankhurst? Haven't you heard of the progress we're making throughout the country with our demonstrations.' she demanded coolly. '*When* we get the vote, this country *and* Newcastle will see big changes - and for the better. You mark my words!' She glanced at him slyly. 'Did you know I have been in prison?'

His eyes opened wide in disbelief and she chuckled at his reaction. 'What happened?' he asked.

She bit neatly through her biscuit and chewed before answering. 'We decided to hold a demonstration to further our cause during Lloyd George's visit to Newcastle. It was peaceful enough at the start but when we reached the station we found the police had set up barricades and were searching every building for known suffragettes. I managed to escape but it's the same story all over the country. It only turns violent when we're up against the coppers. Some of the girls come back with stories of being dragged down side streets, indecently assaulted and having limbs broken. Others are arrested and beaten. Some go on hunger strike and are force fed.' Jane shuddered.

'But you said you were arrested!'

She nodded. 'Yes, but that was two weeks later. The coppers called me in for questioning but I said I didn't know nowt and they couldn't prove anything. so they just let me stew in a cell overnight.' She shuddered again. Obviously it had been a most unpleasant experience. 'I tell you, those women have got some guts!'

'And are you still learning to read and write?'

'Aye. John Stephenson's giving me extra lessons through the week. I think I would like to be a nurse eventually. John thought it was a good idea, me having nursed ma for so long. He says he'll try and find some nursing books for me to read just so as I know a bit more about it.'

He smiled fondly at her. 'You really seem to have found your place in life don't you?'

She looked taken aback by the question. 'Yes, I think I have. Haven't you?'

Wilfrid allowed his gaze to wander up to the ceiling. 'I'm...I'm not sure.' he said thoughtfully, ignoring the chatter and clatter of crockery. He closed his eyes ....

******

..... as he opened his eyes a voice said, 'A cup of tea, Mr. Bainbridge?' He shook his head. He had just had one - hadn't he?

His eyes focused on the ceiling it was different, the smells were different and the noises were different and he sensed that he was no longer in the genteel surroundings of Fenwick's tearooms. He was back in the base hospital surrounded by his fellow casualities. Back to reality.

******

Such were Wilfred Bainbridge's thoughts as days turned into weeks. They transferred him to another hospital, well away from the front line, but the journey was too much for him and the move set him back many weeks. His memories and the small leather bible which he read daily, kept him sane. He grasped at the words of encouragement from doctors who told him he was looking better. Perhaps he would get through this war after all? Yet somehow, deep down, he knew his injuries were too great.

The nurses were so kind, so patient and caring. He tried not to complain because they were so busy but he was in such considerable pain. He could no longer walk as he was only skin and bones. They tried to get him to eat but each time he swallowed he suffered great discomfort. Then the infection set in and Wilfred Bainbridge found he had nothing in reserve with which to fight it.

Confused in mind and weary in body he lay back on his pillows. A nurse passed the bottom of his bed on her way to tend to someone else. She looked drawn and tired. He wondered whether to call her to ask for a wash but couldn't quite work out why he should want to do that. He was all right the way he was. He lay for a while listening to the sounds around him. The man in the bed opposite was having difficulty breathing. Every breath was a rattle in his chest, distressing to listen to. Did he have a mother? A wife? A sweetheart? Someone who would miss him like his mother missed his father, then Lindsay then..........then himself? He was dying, wasn't he? Strangely enough the thought didn't frighten him the way he had thought it would. This part of it was awful. The cries of pain from around the ward, the stench of bodies, the tired nurses and doctors. The suffering of humanity. A time when men ask, "Where is God in all this?" but that was a question Wilfred didn't feel the need to ask, for as he floated in and out of consciousness he was aware of a very familiar Presence. He'd known God from being a tiny boy sitting on his mother's knee listening to his favourite Bible stories. David and Goliath, Samuel and Eli and the miracles of Jesus. They had always been part of his life, but faith in Jesus Christ, as his own personal friend and companion had only developed as he had grown older. Now, in the last few hours, even through his suffering, he was aware of this familiar, comforting companion close by......waiting. He moved his arm, ever so slowly as every movement was painful.

His thoughts turned to his mother. What wouldn't he give to have her here with him now. What wouldn't he give to have those memories part of his life again. His fingers searched for the small leather bible his mother had given him at their last meeting and with a great deal of effort he slid it out from underneath his pillow. There was blood on the pages and he couldn't see the writing as his vision was blurred, but it was comforting to hold something from home. Something that reminded him of the people he knew and of the dear lady who had been thoughtful enough to buy a bible small enough to fit into his uniform pocket.

Wilfred closed his eyes and the sounds of weeping and sight of suffering faded into the background as he held his bible. Robert Middleton would have carefully chosen this for him. Mr Harris would have made out the bill to give to his mother and Miss Mary Bean would have wrapped it. Ah mother! He couldn't bear to think of her sorrow when she learned of his death. Poor mother. First her dear Thomas, then Lindsay and now..... It was easy to think of his father. He was so like his father in temperament. It would be ....so good to......see his father......

The presence of his companion seemed very close to him now. It would

104

be a relief to leave this world of war and suffering for a better place. He could hear voices dimly in the background. 'He won't be with us much longer.' 'Shame. He was a good patient. Never complained.' 'A handsome young soldier.' 'We need more medicine for these young men!

'Come Wilfred.'

He saw the outstretched hand but for a split second he was afraid to take it. Afraid the movement would cause him more pain - but then it didn't matter any more. Slowly his hand reached out towards the One whom he had known and trusted all his life and as the warmth of His fingers touched his own, he released his grip on the bible his mother had bought him. He had no need of it now. For now he was with the One of whom it told!

> *I have fought the good fight. I have finished my cause. I have kept the faith;*
> *henceforth is laid up for me a crown of righteousness.....*
> *(2 Timothy 4:7.)*

PART THREE
THE SHOP ON PILGRIM STREET
1930

After the war ended in 1919, the country was left in a deep state of mourning. A million men had been killed early in life, leaving almost every home in the land grieving for someone. Thousands of broken and wounded service men returned to Britain with memories so bad they were unable to share them. Unfortunately they discovered that war had created its own urgent problems for the businessman at home and any hopes they may have cherished for a peaceful, secure job for the future were dashed.

During the years following the war, prices began rising to an inordinate level hitting the once thriving industries of coal mining, shipbuilding and engineering. Tyneside was more severely affected than elsewhere. Two of Tyneside's biggest Companies, Armstrong's and Vickers were forced to merge due to a drop in demand for munitions and ships: many other factories had to close down or their employees went on to short-time working. Dissatisfaction among the workforce grew. Miners staged a lockout and there were threats of a general strike. Workers who had previously found themselves comfortably off, became unemployed and were forced to seek work elsewhere. The only significant progress in the north-east appeared to be in the construction of the Tyne Bridge, which provided essential employment and strenghtened the links between Newcastle and Gateshead.

Strangely enough this was a time when the north-east saw growth in leisure and recreation, especially since the development of the wireless and cinema. The importance of sporting pursuits saw the further development of football, until it became the north-east's backbone, replacing the local sport of rowing.

Yet in spite of the economic depression, Bainbridge's Store on Market Street continued to expand with the opening of a grocery and provision market and a ladies hairdressing department. This success was due largely to their chairman, Alderman George Bainbridge, Thomas Bainbridge's brother, who had always been the initiator of expansion. The Bible & Tract Depot was fortunate in that this great business man was also one of their Trustees.

It came as a bit of a surprise when, during a Bible & Tract Trustees meeting one Friday morning, this dominating, white-haired figure with his walrus moustache, dismissively waved the doom and gloom over the shops' profits, to one side and, changing the subject completely, announced with great gusto, that in a few months time, Mr Robert Middleton would have completed fifty years as manager of the shop.

At this unexpected announcement, Robert Middleton raised his eyes from the ledger in which he was writing the minutes of their monthly meeting and there was a surprised silence from the eight Trustees gathered around the table.

'Fifty years!' Last year's disastrous profits were immediately forgotten by Mr Crosier. He himself had served conscientiously as a trustee for forty years and he regarded Robert Middleton as part of the fixtures of the Bible & Tract Depot. It was almost impossible to imagine the shop without him. 'My goodness! Have you been here that long?' He stared at Robert Middleton with unconcealed admiration.

A smile played around Robert Middletons mouth. He was rather proud of his service with The Bible & Tract Depot and was, naturally, a little flattered by the attention he was now receiving.

'Fifty years!' Mr Crosier repeated shaking his head. 'We can't let a momentous occasion like this pass unnoticed.'

'If, God willing, I'm spared till then.' Robert Middleton said softly.

Mr Crosier peered at him across the table. Robert was still a fine figure of a man despite his advanced years and his health not being as good as it used to be.

'And it's not many managers who voluntarily reduce their own wages, rather than increase them.' George Bainbridge said subtly bringing the Trustees back to the subject of money.

'Ah! Yes.... well ...the depression affected profits and ....'

George Bainbridge cut across Robert's explanations. 'I see you reduced your salary by £50 last year to help us weather the general fall in trade and again in February this year by another £100.' He flicked over the pages, then looking up at his manager said, with a deep note of sincerity, 'That is most generous of you Mr Middleton. Most generous! However I do not think we, as Trustees, can permit this, especially as your daughter works for here for only seventeen shillings a week and your son's voluntary services are increasing by the week.'

Robert lowered his head feeling embarassed. William's voluntary hours in the shop had, in fact, caused some friction in his family. While Mrs Middleton desired that William would one day take over from his father at The Bible & Tract Depot, William had ideas of his own. He wanted to set up a car sales business but lacked the necessary capital.

'Last year our profit was...' Mr John Watson, the chairman and a Trustee for over thirty-two years glanced down at the papers in front of him, '£146.17s.4d, considerably less than we had hoped for, nevertheless, we do have the small legacy left to us by the late Mr Shipley which I believe would allow your salary to remain at...' he glanced through his papers again, '...at £400 a year. Agreed gentlemen?'

There was a unanimous show of hands and general mutters of agreement.

Robert Middleton cleared his throat with a nervous cough, 'That is most generous of you gentlemen but I would most urgently ask you to reconsider. We are barely managing, especially since we have had to meet a large increase in rates and taxes recently. I would like to recommend that my salary be reduced to £250 per annum.' He held up his hand at the murmurs of dissent. 'At my age gentlemen I have no need for extra money, neither does Mrs Middleton. Hopefully this depression in trade will not be long in passing and I can return to my normal salary.'

There was silence around the table.

'I don't like it.' Mr Crosier remarked bluntly.

George Bainbridge shook his head. 'It's abnormal reducing the wages of our staff.'

John Watson leaned forward, his elbows resting on the highly polished table. 'Could I suggest a compromise?' Without waiting for a reply he continued, 'Perhaps we could start paying your salary at the yearly rate of £250, but review the situation in three months?' He glanced around the table and after a few minutes discussion there was a reluctant show of hands and grateful murmurs of thanks floated in Robert Middletons direction.

'Thank you gentlemen,' Robert Middleton said brusquely. 'Now, Mr Watson has asked me to bring to your attention a most interesting fact.' Mr Middleton caught their attention which, to his relief, meant their focus was no longer on his wages. 'In 1864, Mr Ephraim Lister, the first manager of The Bible & Tract Depot, listed the names of the fifty subscribers of the £200.9s.6d for the opening of the shop in Pilgrim Street. Out of those listed, the only one still living today is Alderman George Bainbridge.'

George Bainbridge raised his eyebrows. 'Really? 1864 eh?' His eyes glazed over as he thoughtfully leant back in his chair. 'Those were the days eh? What!'

'Our warmest congratulations George.' John Watson said heartily.

'Must be....sixty odd years ago?' George Bainbridge's vacant expression left the rest of the present Trustees in no doubt he was still reminiscing over past Trustees - Henry Richardson, Mr Alexander, Joseph Maher, Mr Angus and his own brother Thomas Bainbridge. 'It seems no time at all since.....'

Robert Middleton couldn't help reflect that that was the trouble with the present Trustees. They were all getting older and whereas at one time business matters could be dealt with quickly, there was a tendency nowadays to drift off into the past. He did not of course count himself as being one of the grand old gentlemen of The Bible & Tract Depot.

There were only two other business matters to be dealt with that morning. The first was that Ephraim Listers notes had reminded Robert Middleton that the Tyne and Tees Steam Shipping Company, had been carrying bibles and books "freight free" from London to Newcastle for them since the shop opened over sixty years ago. Even Ephraim Lister himself had frequently travelled "free of charge". Robert felt a letter expressing the grateful thanks of the Trustees would be in order.

The second matter of business was that a shop calling itself "The Bible and Tract Depot" had opened in Blackett Street, leading to confusion in letters, parcels and books. The discussion became quite heated but the Trustees were in unanimous agreement that it was a downright cheek and the immediate course of action should be for Mr Davies, the Depot solicitor and trustee, who was present that morning, to speak to the new owners asking them to adopt another name..

The meeting came to a close with its usual time of prayer, which went on slightly longer than usual, and during which could be heard a few gentle snores, then the Trustees rose and slowly wandered downstairs into the shop. Here some of them stood around talking to John Stephenson before taking their leave of one another.

It was an accepted fact that John Stephenson would be browsing around the books during the Trustees monthly meeting. A quiet, studious gentleman in his late sixties, with gentle faded eyes and a smile warm enough to take your eyes off the ugly red birth mark which stretched from his chin down

109

his neck. He would settle himself on a wooden chair in the corner reading a book until the trustees appeared. Sometimes he would assist behind the counter if they were busy, or deal with one of the customers. When he did, it never failed to amaze Fay Middleton, Robert's daughter, how much he knew about the business. There were times she resented the way he made himself at home but she dared not say anything. He was too highly respected by her father and the Trustees. She sat behind a large counter at the back of the shop with her head bowed over the books, trying to appear inconspicuous but listening to every word.

'Fifty years George said Robert had been manager here.' she heard Mr Crosier say to John Stephenson. 'As I said to the Trustees, we can't let an occasion like this pass unnoticed. Buy him something of course but I wondered if you had any ideas John?'

'Mmm,' John Stephenson rubbed his chin thoughtfully. 'We could ask past members of staff if they would like to contribute or be part of some celebration. I'll have a few words with Jane Gibson. See what she comes up with shall I?'

'I'd appreciate that. Fifty years eh?' Mr Crosier shook his head in amazement. 'I bet you've been coming through these doors just as long eh John?'

John Stephenson smiled. 'Not far short of sixty years for me. It was one of the first trustees, Mr Henry Richardson, who literally dragged me from the gutter, gave me schooling at the age of eight and set me on my feet. I worked in Mr Thomas Bainbridge's Gospel vans for a few years before being employed by the shop as colporteur.' His smile faded. 'Of course the war changed things. There's not the need for colporteurs as there use to be.'

Mr Crosier sighed. 'True enough John. True enough.'

Fay Middleton turned her attention back to her books. She was in her late twenties, small and plump with short dark hair framing a plain round face. She was no beauty and she knew it, but she had a sweet smile and was a quiet and efficient worker.

Robert Middleton made his way through the group of the trustees towards the rows of shelves designated for Sunday Schools and their teachers. This part of the shop had developed slowly but steadily over the years and the growing number of children's tracts and bibles encouraged Sunday School pupils to come and browse. Unfortunately a few of them weren't averse to stealing a few tracts or even the odd bible, so they had to be carefully watched. There were two young boys standing in the corner flicking through one of the large print bibles. Although poorly dressed, Robert was relieved to see their hands were clean as they carefully turned over the pages.

'It'll take years to read through that!' The taller of the two boys said peering over his companions shoulder. 'Y'hear it all at Sunday School anyway, so what's the point in wantin' to read it?' He sniffed and rubbed his nose across the sleeve of his jacket.

'I'm gonna read all the books in the bible wot the teacher telt us about. I divvint wanna miss one oot an' I need to read 'em aal afore I goes to heaven.' The little chap said seriously.

'Why can't y'just read the ones with the good stories in?'

The little fellow shook his head. 'I wouldn't dare.'

'Why not like?'

The little fellow frowned worriedly as he looked up at his companion. 'Well can you imagine getting up there and seeing all them disciples wot you've read about, then this old guy called Habbakuk comes up to you and says, "Ah! But have you read me book son?" You're gonna feel aaful if y' haven't, aren't you?"

Robert Middleton hid a smile and moved across the shop to have a word with his daughter Fay.

******

Jane Gibson stepped neatly off the trolley bus platform into the slushy wet snow and walked as briskly up Grainger Street as the slippery conditions would allow. Now in her early fifties she was smart, slim, and attractive but her story was that of many women who had lost loved ones in the First World War. Yes her Charlie had come back all right, but he wasn't the man she had married. That was why she loved the cinema. It was a world of make-believe and escape and she went regularly, despite the view of many Christians that it was sinful.. She'd even had her hair cut short and fashionable like some of the film stars but then there was no-one now to tell her she looked nice. Charlie used to, before the war but when he returned he hardly noticed her. He died two years after his return, wounded in body and mind and with no sense of hope for the future at all. Many times during those difficult months her thoughts had turned to the handsome young

111

Lieutenant Wilfred Bainbridge who had flirted so outrageously with her. Not that there was any real romance between them, but there again, if he had returned from the war and not Charley, who knows?

As she reached the Bigg Market she spotted her brother Tom. He was standing on the corner with his cloth cap pulled firmly over his head, his hands pushed in his coat pockets and his collar up to protect himself from the icy January weather. There were always men standing around in the streets these days or queuing for work outside factory gates or the labour exchange. Jane's heart ached for them and their families but it was a sign of the times. Further down the Bigg Market a number men huddled together listening to a speaker standing on the monument steps protesting vehemently about the rights of the unemployed, There were always speakers shouting about the rights of the working class these days and there were even plans for a march from Newcastle to London to put pressure on the Government to do something about the high levels of unemployment in the region.

'Tom! Tom!'

The figure turned and saw her and ambled across to where she stood, giving her a twisted smile. It wasn't easy for him being unemployed and having a wife and three children to feed. In fact if it wasn't for the odd hand-outs from his sister, he and his family would be in a bad way.

'Happy New Year sis. At least I hope it will be, for all of us. Day off work?'

She nodded wondering why he never could remember the hospital always gave her Fridays off. 'I have to work this week-end though. How are May and the kids?'

'Fine. Just hoping I'll find work soon. Dunno how much longer we can keep on like this. Will you keep your ears open for work at the hospital.'

'Yes I will.' She rummaged in her bag and slipped him a few coins. He smiled embarrassed but gratefully as they parted.

Jane Gibson couldn't help reflect how fortunate she was in many respects. When the First World War broke out Emmeline Pankhurst, the suffragette, had suspended all militancy and called upon her followers to help defend the country. The only thing Jane knew how to do was sell books and she had no desire to work in the factories making arms and munitions, but after seeing an advert in the window of the Labour Exchange for people interested in nursing, she answered the appeal and was accepted for basic training. In 1918, the House of Commons decided that women, at least those aged 30 years and older, really were equal to men as they were given the vote. Many of them, however, lost their jobs when the men returned from the war. It had taken them nearly forty years to reach their objective. It had taken Jane Gibson only a few weeks to realise that nursing came naturally to her and that this was what she wanted to do for the rest of her life. After all she had had plenty practice, what with her mother and Charley.

As Jane turned the corner into Blackett Street, she was surprised to see Mr Davies, one of the Trustees, gazing into the window of a small book shop, which oddly enough sported the name "The Bible and Tract Depot" on the front. He hesitated for a moment, then squaring his shoulders and lifting his chin as if ready for battle, he opened the shop door and walked inside. Jane smiled to herself wishing she'd been a fly on the wall at the Trustees meeting. She wouldn't mind betting there must have been some choice words said about this shop, which was just around the corner, from the Pilgrim Street shop with the same name. She crossed over the street, avoiding the tram rails and peered through the shop window. Not that she could see or hear much but judging from the waving arms the conversation appeared to be turning quite heated. This was quite surprising as Mr Davies, the solicitor, was normally quite a cool-headed sort of man. She smiled to herself and reluctantly leaving them to it, she took the short walk around the corner to The Bible & Tract Depot in Pilgrim Street.

Robert Middleton had called upon her occasionally to help them out during their busy periods when she wasn't on duty at the hospital. The shop had changed quite a bit since her day but there were still a number of familiar faces, including John Stephenson. She liked John Stephenson.

William Middleton greeted her with a smile when she entered the shop, but then William greeted everyone with a smile. He was a pleasant, dark-haired young man in his thirties, of medium height and build, with the same attractive features as his father. In the past year he had taken over a substantial amount of his father's work as Secretary.

'Ah! Miss Gibson.' John Stephenson smiled down at her and her face broke into a wide grin. 'I was just talking about you to Mr Crosier.'

'Something good I hope.' she said, raising her eyebrows.

'Absolutely, because there's nothing bad about you Miss Gibson, although,' John lowered his voice and said in a confiding manner, 'there are some stories about your time working here that could well shock the present day staff.'

Jane laughed. But then John always did have the ability to make her laugh.

Sensing Fay Middleton's eyes upon them, John took Jane by the arm and steered her towards the back of the shop. Lowering his voice he said, 'Mr Crosier has just informed me that in March, Mr Middleton will have been manager here for fifty years. He has asked if we could organise something special for him. So I wondered about contacting past members of staff and perhaps having a party. What do you think?'

Jane rested her hand lightly on his arm. 'What a brilliant idea John! Perhaps, we could all pool together to buy him something really nice. Oh yes! I like the idea.'

'Could I treat you to a cup of tea at Bainbridge's and we can make our plans? Of course, if it's not convenient....?' John added seeing her slight hesitation.

'No. That would be lovely. Thank you. I just thought that it would be more sensible for you to come to my house for tea instead. I have my address book at home so then we'd be sure not to miss anyone out.'

John smiled a big wide smile. 'That sounds ideal. I'd like that. Thank you.' and wondered why an old bachelor like himself should suddenly feel quite excited at the prospect of tea at Jane Gibson's house. There was a decided spring in his step as, business and niceties completed, they left the shop together.

******

Henrietta Harris stood nervously by the window waiting for Kate Bainbridge. It seemed as if she had spent all her life waiting for friends, or her family, to come and take her somewhere or other. She had never been blessed with good health, but since her nervous breakdown she had never found it easy to go out, never mind go back into the shop again - not until today. Today was different. She wasn't going to the shop to work but to a tea-party to celebrate fifty years of Robert Middleton being manager of The Bible & Tract Depot. As she fidgeted with the collar of her coat she spotted Kate Bainbridge's chauffeur-driven car pulling up at her front door. Pulling on her gloves she gave herself a last, withering glance in the mirror above the fireplace.

'Come on Henrietta!' she said to herself. 'Pull yourself together. You can do this!' Then, taking a deep breath, she closed the door firmly behind her.

******

George Bainbridge was rushed off his feet, but then George Bainbridge was always rushed off his feet. There was no doubt in the minds of his staff at Bainbridge's, that despite the man being a workaholic and a bit of a tyrant, they owed their jobs to him. It was therefore a bit of a surprise one Friday afternoon, when he informed his Managing Director that he was taking the afternoon off as he had a previous and most important tea-party to attend. His Managing Director assured him he was well able to cope and breathed a sigh of relief when the door closed behind him.

******

The celebratory tea-party was to be held in the big room above the shop so it was extremely difficult for William and Fay Middleton to keep Robert Middleton out the way while food was ferried upstairs by Jane Gibson.

The Trustees had asked Robert to stay behind that evening after closing the shop to present him with a small token of their appreciation for his fifty years of service as manager. But, judging from the stifled giggles from little Miss Wilson, the new delivery girl and the way William kept dragging him to the back of the shop to look at Sunday School books, the staff had something up their sleeve as well. He hoped they didn't make too much of a fuss. He glanced at his watch. It was just turned half-past three. Two-and a-half hours to go before the Trustees arrived. Robert Middleton felt strangely tense but it wasn't a bad feeling. There was something rather pleasant about the way they wanted to show their appreciation for his fifty years as manager.

The bell tinkled as the shop door opened. He turned and was surprised to see Mr Davies, the shop's solicitor and a Trustee enter.

'I wonder if I could have a word Mr Middleton,' he said. 'In private.' he added.

'Yes of course. Come upstairs to the office and we can....'

'No, no, no. It is with regard to the other Bible and Tract Depot in Blackett Street. I thought perhaps we could take a short walk around there.

115

I would like your opinion on their supposed change of name.'

'Well....I'm afraid I'm rather...'

'I really would appreciate it Mr Middleton. When your staff are affected by this shop....'

Robert Middleton glanced at his watch again. 'My staff? Ah! Well, yes of course Mr Davies.' He reached for his coat behind the long counter where Fay sat doing the books and administration work. 'I won't be long.' he informed her.

She nodded without taking her eyes off the figures in the ledger. 'Certainly, father.'

The other Bible & Tract Depot was just around the corner but both men walked slowly. Neither were as fast as they used to be.

'Mr Sinclair, the owner, appears to be digging his heels in with regard to the name of the shop.' Mr Davies confided. 'It is four months since my last conversation with him and the only change he has made to the name is a new board above his window.'

They rounded the corner into Blackett Street and stood surveying the new board which carried the words, "The Northern Bible & Tract Depot."

'I think it is still unacceptable.' Mr Davies continued. 'Wouldn't you agree?'

'I do agree with you Mr Davies. The Post Office frequently deliver books, parcels and letters to the wrong address because of the similarity in names. It's just not good enough!'

The two men stood discussing the problem and watched several customers enter the front of the rival shop. No wonder profits were down if they were losing customers like this. Something would really have to be done about it. Then Mr Davies, begging a previous appointment, took leave of Robert Middleton, who wandered slowly and thoughtfully back to his own shop in Pilgrim Street.

The bell rang as he opened the door and the hubbub of voices from the crowd of people in his shop stopped abruptly. Robert stood in the doorway blinking in surprise.

It was Caroline he spotted first. She was wearing her best coat and hat and smiled at the look of amazement on his face. Then she moved over to his side, closing the door behind him.

'Congratulations Mr Middleton!' Alderman George Bainbridge barked. 'Thought you had to wait till the shop closed at six didn't you? Hah!' he chuckled. 'Your staff had other ideas I can tell you.'

Still speechless, Robert allowed his eyes to wander over the assembled crowd and he picked out the familiar and well-loved smiling faces of the Trustees and staff he had managed over the years. There was Ruth Grigs, who had spent years popping in to help them during times of staff sickness or particularly busy periods. She was looking old and frail now as she was in her seventies and there was Kate Bainbridge, still a handsome and well-dressed woman, also in her seventies. She inclined her head elegantly towards him and her lips parted in a smile just for him. Who was that standing beside her? My goodness! Henrietta Harris! His face lit up at the sight of her and Henrietta flushed with delight at being recognised. She was suddenly very pleased that she had come. His eyes picked out Henry Harris, his manager while he was away in London or Leeds on business. He moved over to him, his hand outstretched. 'Henry! My dear fellow.'

The door bell rang behind him and in came Mr Davies, with a broad grin on his face. 'I thought I'd never keep you out of the shop long enough for everyone to arrive! Congratulations on fifty years as manager Mr Middleton!'

His son William crossed the crowded shop floor and closing the door behind Mr Davies placed the "closed" sign to the outside.

Robert glanced at his watch. 'William you can't....'

'Yes I can father.,' replied William, 'Special permission from the Trustees. Now shall we all move upstairs, there's a tea-party especially in your honour.'

Jane Gibson was organising young Miss Wilson to pour out the teas and there was another woman, who was busy taking the covers off an appetising display of cakes, sandwiches and scones. The face was strangely familiar to Robert Middleton. My goodness! It was Miss Bean! She'd been delivery girl here when Wilfred Bainbridge was alive. He must have a word with her. She was looking quite the elegant young lady these days!

'Mr and Mrs Middleton. Do sit down and have a cup of tea.' John Stephenson pulled out two chairs and Fay brought over a plate of sandwiches.

Robert Middleton seemed to be in a rather pleasant and surreal state where he was no longer in control of what was taking place. He wanted to say "What about the shop?", but the staff, both present and past, seemed to have everything planned between them. So, with Caroline clasping his hand,

117

he sat and listened to the history of The Bible & Tract Depot as told by Alderman George Bainbridge and the important role that he, Robert, had played in its development. George Bainbridge, on behalf of the Trustees, then presented him with a magnificient clock.

Robert was about to give a speech of thanks when John Stephenson stood up.

'I've never given a speech before.' he admitted. John spoke quietly and shuffled, a little embarrassed at being the focus of attention. 'But it is fitting and seemly that I do so on this very special occasion as one with perhaps the longest memories of The Bible and Tract Depot.' He glanced at Jane who gave him a smile of encouragement. 'There's not much I can say that Mr Bainbridge hasn't already said, except that as I worked here as colporteur in the past, I feel my success was due to three men. The first, Henry Richardson, who took me off the streets and educated me. The second, Thomas Bainbridge who inspired new ideas in the north-east and in me. And the third man was you, Mr Middleton sir, who made the openings for these new ideas and encouraged your staff to greater things. On behalf of the staff, past and present I would like to present you with a small memento of our deep affection and respect. The Bible and Tract could not have wished for a better manager than your good self sir.'

Robert felt a lump in his throat as he received the small neat vase the staff had bought for him. He cleared his throat. 'I'm...I'm...' he swallowed hard, 'Ladies and gentlemen. This has been a....a... I am most grateful for your gifts and for all your kind words. I have tried to do my best to serve you as manager. Through the good times, the amusing times and the difficult ones. But to see you all here to wish me well.....I am deeply moved ..deeply moved....' He stopped. Someone started to applaud, then Fay came up and although not normally a demonstrative girl there were tears in her eyes as she hugged him. Kate Bainbridge dabbed her nose with her handkerchief came over and gave him a kiss on the cheek. George Bainbridge heartily shook his hand as did the other Trustees and Henrietta Harris just stood in the corner, beside her father, weeping tears of happiness.

John Stephenson made his way over to Jane Gibson, who was sitting in a corner with a plate of sandwiches balanced on her knees and a cup ot tea in her hand. Bending over he whispered to her, 'Was that alright, Jane?' Her hair tickled his cheek when she looked up at him. 'It was a lovely speech John. Really lovely.'

Helping himself to some sandwiches, a cake and a cup ot tea, John sat down beside her and said. 'I think the afternoon has turned out to be a success, don't you?'

'I do John. We should pat ourselves on the back. I think we did a very good job.'

'Mmm.' he said thoughtfully. 'We work well as a team.' He watched the young delivery girl chatting amiably to the elderly Miss Grigs.

'I shall miss our afternoon teas together now that this party is over.' intimated John. 'I find you very pleasant company and I just wish that we had another one to organise.'

Jane Gibson raised her eyebrows.

'Considering the difference in our ages we get on remarkably well together. Wouldn't you say so?' he added.

'Yes, John.' she said slowly, 'We always have.'

Brushing a few crumbs from his coat John looked Jane in the eye and said, 'I think it would be a nice idea to see what else we could enjoy doing together.'

'John Stephenson, are you flirting with me?' said Jane, in mock surprise.

He chuckled. 'I'm not sure. I've never done it before.'

Jane smiled at him, 'Take my word for it. You are!'

'And you don't mind?'

'Of course not!'

'And you don't mind about the age....thing.'

'No John dear. I don't mind about the age thing at all.'

Robert Middleton's fingers ached with so much shaking hands. It was hard to believe so many people had turned up just for him, especially the Trustees when they had businesses of their own to run. And Henrietta Harris was very brave to have ventured out, for the occasion. Then there was dear Miss Ruth Grigs. She was walking badly these days, it must have been quite an effort for her. John Stephenson and Jane Gibson sat closely together smiling happily. Everyone was chatting as though they were life-long friends when in actual fact some of them barely knew each other. Perhaps working in a Christian book shop drew everyone together in a way that was different to anywhere else. Then there was Caroline. Dear Caroline. He looked down at her. A strict, no-nonsense sort of person and certainly not one given to emotionalism, but there were tears in her eyes as she looked up at him. 'I am so proud of you Robert.' she whispered. 'You have made a truly great manager for this shop.' And that was praise enough for Robert Middleton.

1936: The Jarrow March

It hadn't been such a bad day when they'd set off. A bit on the cool side but that was to be expected in October. Tom Gibson's wife May and his sister, had waited anxiously by the side of the road watching Tom and the other men preparing to make the long three hundred mile march south, towards the capital city. Then they lost sight of him. He was somewhere in the midst of that solid mass of grey clothes, black mufflers and cloth caps.

Tom, like hundreds of other men from Jarrow and other towns in the north-east who had lost their jobs due to the closure of the shipyards, had been forced to take some form of action to bring the plight of the industrial northern working man to the attention of the government. The two hundred men chosen for the march had left amidst cheers and cries of encouragement from other workers, members of the public, wives and sweethearts. There had been a strong sense of being united in a common cause, but now, two weeks into the march, they were wet and cold, following the heavy rain which had drenched them earlier that morning. With blisters on both feet from his ill-fitting boots, Tom Gibson was feeling rather despondent.

'You're too old to go gallivanting off to London luv.' his wife May had reproved him. 'Leave it to the young'uns.'

'If we all took that attitude May, we'd get nowt done!' He had stormed around their tiny kitchen in the back-to-back house where they lived, knowing she was right yet desperately longing to be one of the chosen marchers.

May had sighed. She was a small slight woman who had borne the brunt of trying to feed her family during the years of depression, yet she had always managed to retain a positive attitude despite days of hunger. Her favourite comment was 'God'll provide for us Tom. Divvint fret!' but in Tom's eyes, God wasn't doing a very good job of it! If it hadn't been for their Jane slipping him the odd bob or so, May's own thriftiness in keeping house and the odd bit of scrounging work here and there by himself and his eldest son, they would be dying of starvation by now!

With a sigh of relief he saw the long line of men in front of him turning into a field. That meant it was time for their mid-day grub. The organisers of the Jarrow March had provided them with their own special bus to store their kit bags, kitchen equipment and half a dozen cooks. Halfway between the day's starting point and planned finishing point the bus would pull into a field and with the farmers permission, set up the kitchen and wait for the men to arrive for their mid-day snack.

Tom followed the crocodile of men into the field, picked up his sandwiches and mug of tea and looked around for somewhere to sit. The grass was still wet but he spotted a chap he'd got talking to after they'd passed through Durham, sitting on a tree stump at the edge of the field examining his boots. He looked up as Tom approached.

'I divvint think I'm gonna make it mate." he said wearily. 'It's me boots. They were holed afore I even started. Look! There's hardly any boot left!'

Tom sank down wearily beside his companion. 'There's a few'o the men in the same state but I heard tell the Co-op are gonna mend aal wor boots.' He took mouthful of his cheese sandwich and a sip of hot sweet tea before adding, 'No doubt they don't want us looking like a lotta tramps when we reach London to hand in wor petition.' His companion raised his eyebrows in surprise. 'New boots eh?' Tom watched with some amusement as his companion, encouraged by the thought of a pair of mended boots, tucked into his thick crusty cheese sandwich with renewed vigour.

May had put a few sandwiches up for him before he left the north-east but he'd eaten those within the first couple of hours and other than the first night, when the promised hot meal from a local council turned out to be corned beef sandwiches, they'd done quite well for food on the journey down. Once the newspapers and wireless caught hold of the story of the "Jarrow Hunger March", the country began to sit up and take notice as the marchers headed their way. Was it the Ferryhill miners or the Yorkshire miners who laid on that magnificent breakfast of ham and eggs and tomatoes for them? Tom couldn't remember, but he was conscious of the fact that for many of them, this had been the best meal they had eaten for months. Unfortunately the main problem had been the horribly blistered feet of men who were unused to such long hours of walking.

'You said you were from Jarrow?' Tom asked his companion.

'Aye. I telt yer mate. It's serious doon our way.'

Tom nodded understandingly, then reaching inside his pocket pulled out an old rag and a newspaper. 'How about wrapping yer foot in this and stuffing yer boot with the newspaper?'

The man looked dubiously at both items. 'Ye must be mad! Walkin' t' London on a newspaper? Well it'll do till we get wor boots fixed, anyways it's all in a good cause eh?' he said.Then he shrugged and stuffed the remaining part of his sandwich in his mouth.

'Aye. All in a good cause mate.' Tom said.

******

Starting a new "Minutes Book" always took longer than expected as the names of all the current Trustees had to be entered in the front page. William Middleton flicked through the old ledger as the Trustees arrived into the Committee Room for their meeting. It had fallen open at two entries made in May 1930, six years ago. He had read them before, but somehow finishing the ledger and storing it away made it feel like the end of an era:

> *12th May 1930*
> *This is the first Trustees' Meeting that Robert Middleton has been unable to attend during his fifty one years of service at the Depot. He was under doctor's orders not to be present The acting secretary, William Middleton, was thanked for stepping in for his father.*

A few days later, much to the shock of his family and The Bible & Tract Depot, Robert Middleton died.

> *20th May 1930: Special Meeting:*
> *The Trustees desire to place on record their sincere regret at the loss they have sustained by the death of Mr Robert Middleton, who for nearly fifty-one years has been Manager of the depot. They would like to express their warm appreciation of his loyal, diligent and successful management over this long period. Further, they wish to convey to his family, their deep sympathy at their bereavement.*

William Middleton closed the old ledger book. It was like closing a chapter of his father's life, for indeed The Bible & Tract Depot had been Robert's life - his and Caroline's. That was the trouble really. Ma-ma, as he and Fay referred to Caroline, could be so domineering. She seemed determined to make it William and Fay's life also.

'It's a good firm to work for William. Both your father and I have reason to be grateful to them. Look at their generosity to me after Robert died.'

William would never forget that morning a few days after Robert's funeral. He, Fay and and his mother had met with two of the Trustees, Alderman George Bainbridge and Mr Charles Dymond, J.P.

'This is the very least we can do, my dear Mrs Middleton.' George Bainbridge had said, handing her an envelope.

Caroline opened the envelope and her hand went to her mouth in shocked surprise when she pulled out the cheque. William had walked over to her and looked over her shoulder. When he had seen that the cheque was for a substantial sum of money, he had looked questioningly at George Bainbridge.

'Your husband, your er...father, took a substantial reduction in his salary during the depression years.' George Bainbridge had explained. 'So would you please accept the cheque with our grateful thanks and er...and our deepest sympathy.'

Caroline's normally stiff composure had crumbled slightly and she had been near to tears as she stammered her gratitude.

George Bainbridge had suggested that the amount could be used to buy the house in Ryton that husband Robet had expressed an interest in at one time.

Caroline had indeed bought the house in Ryton and William had offered to continue as acting manager until a replacement was found. However, pressure from mama and Fay had eventually worn him down and he had surrendered to the inevitable - he became the full-time manager.

His wife Olive had admonished him for seeming to be persuaded, against his will, to take the position but, strangely enough, after a few weeks in the job full-time he began to realise that he had the skills to bring the managing of the shop up to-date and even began to enjoy the work. The greatest surprise to him was how responsive Fay, who held the post of book-keeper, was to his role on manager, although he suspected this had more to do with mama's drilling than anything else.

It was a busy morning but then William expected it to be as there was a full agenda. Alderman George Bainbridge, the Chairman, had returned tanned from his annual trip to Norway, where he had spent his time fishing

123

with the family. He was brimming over with an arm-stretching tale of his record catch - a fifty seven and a half pound salmon. Eventually he got round to Trustee business and reported that it had been another profitable year for The Bible & Tract Depot. This was put down to the publication of the new Methodist Hymnbook and the opening in the basement of a permanent Sunday School Department. Charles Dymond J.P., another Trustee, said he hoped next year would be just as profitable with the coronation of Edward, the new King, to which they all nodded their heads in agreement. William kept his head down. He didn't completely approve of the new King who appeared to be involved with a divorced woman, and an American at that! Bringing the Trustees back to the business in-hand, William informed them that the most popular book on their lists was "Pilgrim's Progress", which was followed by "Aesop's Fables", "Gulliver's Travels" and "Arabian Nights". The Trustees noted with satisfaction that Bunyan's book had been a best seller since the day the Depot opened.

The Trustees then discussed plans for the proposed extensive alterations to the shop front and it had been estimated that the cost would be not less than £1,000. While this fact pleased the Trustees, William was more anxious about the burden likely to be placed on his staff during these alterations.

'I wonder if it would be possible to use the services of Mr Gibson to assist the staff in the general heavy work once the alterations have been completed?' William asked quietly. Seeing the blank expression crossing the faces of the Trustees he added, 'Mr Tom Gibson is the brother of Jane Gibson who used to work here. He has helped us out with odd jobs in the past.'

'Ah, yes! Now I place the fellow.' George Bainbridge answered. 'Small, stocky chap. Did a good job assembling shelves and painting the basement for us. Yes, by all means see if he is available to help out for a few days when the work is finished Mr Middleton. Agreed gentlemen?' He looked around the table for agreement and there were general nods of the head with the exception of Charles Dymond who was stroking his chin thoughtfully.

'I have a vague recollection of seeing the man with the Jarrow Marchers a couple of weeks ago.' he said.

George peered at him above his rimmed spectacles. 'Yes, well Charles, I would imagine he'd be back by the time we eventually get round to starting the extensions.' he remarked dryly.

'Possibly, possibly.' Charles replied absently, then added. 'I think we should remember them in our prayers this morning gentlemen.'

'Who?' George asked.

'The Jarrow Marchers and Mr Gibson. In their own way they are attempting to draw attention to the plight of the poor here in the north, by a march to the capital city. A brave thing to do, especially in weather like this!' He glanced out of the window to the steady downpour that had been with them all morning. 'Yes,' he added. 'I think they need our prayers gentlemen.'

George Bainbridge solemnly picked up the bible beside him and turning over the pages, read part of Psalm 86. 'Hear O Lord and answer me, for I am poor and needy. Guard my life for I am devoted to you.' He paused thoughtfully. 'Let us pray gentlemen.'

******

The Jarrow Marchers, carrying their "Jarrow Crusade" banner continued their march through the towns and villages with the men playing their "mouthies" (mouth-organs). Crowds came out to greet them on their journey and there were packets of sandwiches and even offers of jobs. But the men stayed resolute to their cause of reaching London with their petition. At times they were joined by little Ellen Wilkinson, M.P. for Jarrow, although she didn't march every step of the way with them. Much as they admired her, their pace slowed considerably when she appeared on the scene to march with them. At other times she tended blistered feet and encouraged the men in their walk. It was no wonder they loved her.

As one of the oldest men on the march, Tom was managing far better than he had expected. But then he had always been one for walking and keeping fit. Now it was standing him in good stead.

The weather had improved since they had finished their mid-day snack and cup of tea. The grey clouds had dispersed and a warm milky sun penetrated easily through the thin white layer that was left. He had found the brisk pace the men had adopted over the past two weeks comfortable and there was always someone to chat to or the occasional song to join in which helped pass the time. He had time to think when he was on the move as well, especially when miles of countryside stretched before them and there were no cries of encouragement and the next meal was three or four hours away. Nevertheless, the march was no picnic. Months of being deprived of good wholesome food had taken its toll on all the men and there were a number of them in quite bad shape.

The sun broke through into a layer of blue sky. He pulled his cap off and shoved it into his jacket pocket to enjoy the warmth on the top of his head. He glanced over the hedge to a field full of cabbages. By gum! The crowds at Newgate Street vegetable Market would give a pretty penny for cabbages that size! As he marched his mind drifted back to the first time he was hired to do some work for The Bible & Tract Depot....

******

Tom loved Newgate Street Market, where shoppers were enticed by calls of "Fresh vegetables!" and "Get yer fresh vegetables here!" and skilfully avoided cars heading towards the new Tyne Bridge which had been opened by King George V a few years ago. It was in this busy place that he had spotted Mr Middleton Junior.

'Excuse me sir.' he had said removing his cloth cap. He had always been in awe of the people of The Bible & Tract Depot. He felt they were a cut above the likes of himself. Tom wasn't an educated man, could barely read or write and his whole life had been spent in and out of work - mainly out! Whereas he felt the selling bibles and religious books must make the staff of the Depot, quite holy.

William Middleton had stopped. 'Yes er...Mr Gibson isn't it?'

'Yes sir. It is sir.'

'What can I do for you?'

'Well sir. Our Jane, me sister like. Telt me you was perhaps looking for someone to help clear up and do odd jobs after the builders have gone from the basement of the shop, so I was wondering like, if you needed someone to come in for the odd morning? Any time suiting yourself would do' He had clutched his cap nervously as if his very life depended upon William's answer, and in fact it almost did. May had been distraught at how little she had been able to buy at the grocers that week and bread and dripping had been back on the menu again for a couple of days.

William Middleton had hesitated. Since the competition in Blackett Street had left, turnover had increased so the shop could probably well afford this man's services.

'Yes, Mr Gibson. We would value your services greatly. The basement is in a state of chaos since the alterations and my poor staff are besides themselves trying to sort everything out. There are shelves to be put up and lino to be laid and..' he shook his head despairingly. Tom Gibson's face lit up. 'Thank y' sir. Divvint fret! I'll soon sort yer owt!'

William had given him a warm smile. 'We would appreciate your help. Perhaps you could call in later today and we can come to some arrangement?'

They would appreciate *his* help! 'I will sir. Thank you very much sir!'

William Middleton had turned to hurry away, stepped in a puddle and was hooted at by an impatient driver in his car.

Tom had walked back home. Even catching the tram these days had turned into a luxury. Besides which, he liked walking.

May had greeted him with the words, 'Any luck?' He couldn't help reflect how that had become a regular mode of greeting between him and May in the past few years.

'Aye. Mr Middleton says to call in this afternoon and he'll give me odd jobs to do like the shelving and laying lino.'

'Thank God!' May had muttered, then, 'There's a few odd jobs could be done here first though!' she reproached.

'OK pet, I'll get on to them as soon as I'm not busy at the shop.'

May Gibson had smiled to herself. She could tell he was as pleased as punch at getting work, even if it was only for a few days. She'd best not nag him. Not today!

All she had said was, 'Well if you're going into town again this afternoon, call in at "Dirty Dick's" for some more of that ointment for me legs pet?' Dirty Dick's as it was locally known, was a chemist shop on Clayton Street which stored every medicine imaginable - and it was cheap.

He had found the staff at the Depot weren't such a stuffy, stuck up bunch as he had expected when he turned up for work that afternoon. They had offered him a cup of tea which he didn't have to pay for and they had all been very friendly. Mr Middleton kept popping down to see how things were progressing and to ask if there was anything he needed. None of them seemed to look down on him because he could hardly read or write and they all seemed genuinely concerned about him being unemployed. As the week progressed he began to feel a bit more comfortable around these "holy" people.

127

It was on the Friday morning that the Trustees had come downstairs. He'd almost finished laying the linoleum when the thud of many feet on the stairs to the basement had made him look up in surprise. Seeing who it was he had stood to attention and pulled off his cap.

'Ah! Mr Gibson isn't it?' George Bainbridge barked in his usual loud manner.

Tom was surprised. How on earth did this man know who he was? 'Yes sir.' he muttered. Had he done something wrong? Was he in trouble?

Their eyes wandered around the newly-painted walls and the shelves and as they examined the new floor covering there were murmurs of approval.

'You've made an excellent job of the decorating Mr Gibson. We are indebted to you.' Mr Charles Dymond said softly.

Tom Gibson had given some indistinguishable reply. In all his working life, no-one, but no-one had ever praised his workmanship. Then Alderman George Bainbridge, the great, successful store owner himself had come up for a chat.

'Are you a fishing man?' he'd asked him.

'Aye." he answered. "A bit of a one." he laughed nervously. 'I likes to catch the tiddlers in Saltwell Park.'

'Saltwell....Oh yes. Ever done any sea fishing Mr Gibson?'

'Well, I was fishin' off Tynemouth pier once.

'Off Tynemouth pier eh? Grand place to fish. You would have enjoyed my fishing trip to Norway. The family go salmon fishing there every year. I tell you, the size of the fish that can be caught in those waters....'

'Mr Bainbridge?' He was interrupted in his fishing tale by Charles Dymond.

'Er...Yes? Yes?'

'Perhaps we should allow Mr Gibson to continue his work.'

'Ah! Yes.' George Bainbridge had patted him on the shoulder. 'Forgive me dear man. I'm stopping the good work eh?'

They were real gentlemen they were. Normally men of their class would ignore the likes of him but not only had they admired his handiwork but they'd not thought themselves too high and mighty to stop and pass the time of day with him. Yes - real gentlemen they were.

'God'll provide.' was what May had always said and despite his snort of disbelief every time she came out with it, he had to admit that the week he had worked in The Bible & Tract Depot had certainly seen them over a very bad patch. But it had been more than the money that he had received He had been made to feel that he was somebody, They had considered his well being. Perhaps, that experience had given him the courage to go on the march.

******

Tom was disturbed from his reverie by some clapping and cheering from a group of women standing at the roadside. The marchers were entering the outskirts of another town so there would be a hot meal and place to stay for the night. He might even have a letter from May. It wouldn't be long. Like him, she could barely read or write but it would be nice to see her familiar scrawl again. Perhaps May was right and God was providing after all. Not just for him but for all the other ordinary decent men in the north-east who had been deprived of a living through circumstances beyond their control. God was using this march to have His say about injustice and poverty.

World War Two

On the 10th December 1936, two weeks before Christmas, King Edward V111 put his signature to a document which had been drawn up for his abdication of the throne. The following evening the King, now "His Royal Highness Prince Edward" broadcast a farewell message to an incredulous nation and his younger brother became the new King George V1.

The coronation on the 12th May 1937, was a grand affair and the City of Newcastle upon Tyne rose to the occasion in a big way. Northumberland Street, Grainger Street, Blackett Street and Pilgrim Street were lined with ribbons, buntings and flags. Fenwick's Department Store and Bainbridge's were ablaze of red, white and blue. There were street parties - with games, bonfires and fireworks - in the suburbs, where tables laden with food and drink were devoured by celebrating communities. The people put aside their disappointment over Edward's abdication and took to their hearts the brave naval officer who was now being crowned King George V1.

William felt sorry for the new King. Talk about being thrown in at the deep end, especially when hovering in the background was Adolf Hitler with his aggressive policies in Europe. There was also a new British Prime Minister struggling to avoid another war by using a policy of appeasement to achieve agreement with Germany. All to no avail. In September 1939, a shocked nation listened to the new King solemnly broadcast a message on the wireless.

> *For the second time in the lives of most of us we are at war.*
> *Over and over again we have tried to find a peaceful way out*
> *of the differences between ourselves and those who are now*
> *our enemies, but it has been in vain. We have been forced*
> *into conflict.*

The weeks following the King's announcement were ones of great conflict for William. How did he feel about war and killing a fellow human being? *Could* he kill? How did other Christians come to terms with Christ's teachings of "Thou shalt not kill"? Was it fear making him hide behind his faith? Would he be looked upon as a coward if he didn't offer his services for the military? Being in his forties it would be the younger men who would be called up first, nevertheless, for the first time in his life he, along with many others had to come to terms with what they believed in. The new King, whom William admired so much, spoke frequently on the radio, encouraging his people to fight to retain their way of life. William held the sanctity of life dear to his heart and no matter how hard he prayed, he continued to agonise over the problem.

Meanwhile there was a business at No.14 Pilgrim Street to run which had now been made much more difficult because Herr Hitler wanted to take over the world!

******

Fay Middleton was just thinking of closing the shop for the evening when the door bell tinkled. She smiled when she saw it was her brother. He looked tired. 'How was London?' she asked.

He threw his hat on the clothes stand in the corner. 'Grim!' he answered.

'Oh?'

He sank down on the wooden chair by the counter. 'I seemed to spend half my time in air raid shelters and the other half attending boring meetings.

On top of which the train back to Newcastle was late because of rail lines being bombed. I tell you Fay, this country's falling apart at the seams! If Hitler were to march over us today, there's little or nothing we could do about it!'

'Oh William!' Fay lowered her voice. 'Don't talk like that. Not in front of the staff.'

She looked worriedly into her brother's drawn face. It wasn't like him to be such a defeatist. He was normally such a positive person. 'What's really upset you?'

He sighed. 'I suppose it's....' he stopped, his attention drawn to the two shop girls whispering behind the display table and glancing in his direction. 'Is there a problem ladies?' he queried.

They were both pretty girls in their early twenties, trained staff and hard workers. They came up to him nervously. The taller of the two clasped her hands tightly together and stepped forward as spokeswoman.

'Mr Middleton, we're really sorry about this but....' she hesitated and her companion gave her a sharp nudge from behind as encouragement. 'Well it's like this see. Me and Mavis, well...with the war being on and everyone doing their bit like, well we thought we'd better do something so er....well we've gone and joined up.' Both girls glanced at Fay then at William. 'Sorry an' all that. I know it's leaving you in the lurch especially with all the clearing up to do after the alterations to the shop but... but..... it's the war.' she concluded lamely and looked so pathetically guilty William couldn't help but warm to her.

'*Both* of you leaving!' Fay couldn't hide her displeasure at this bad news.

'I'm afraid so. We were waiting for you to come back from London, Mr Middleton, before we handed in our notice.'

William ran his fingers wearily over his forehead. Although he had half expected to lose some of his staff to military service, this was really the last thing he wanted to hear after such a stressful trip, but he smiled as he said, 'I'm delighted to hear of your commitment ladies and don't worry about us. I'm sure we will manage.'

The eyes of the smaller of the girls brimmed with tears. 'It's not that we don't like working for you Mr Middleton and we do feel bad about letting you down. It's just...just....'

'The war!' concluded Fay sharply.

'Yes.' She shuffled awkwardly on her high-heeled shoes.

Fay took a deep breath. It was obvious William was too tired to deal with this matter tonight. 'Thank you for your concern for the shop.' she said as pleasantly as possible while her mind swam with the consequences of what this would do to them. Finding replacements was extremely difficult these days. 'You must of course do as your conscience bids you.' She glanced at the clock behind the counter. 'Now ladies, it's late, you'll miss your buses if you don't hurry.'

'Thank you Miss Middleton, Mr Middleton.'

'Thank you for being so understanding.'

Fay followed them to the shop door, closed it behind them, then pulled down the blackout shutters and turned back to where her brother sat sprawled out on the hard wooden chair with his eyes closed.

'So the trip was a waste of time and money.' It was a statement rather than a question.

William yawned and rubbed his eyes. 'What do you think? The publishing industry is on the decline and there's paper rationing. The only good thing about my trip to London was being able to purchase a few special lines for the shop and ...oh er, yes.....' He eased himself into an upright position. 'Guess who I travelled down to London with on the train?'

'No idea. Who?' She began tidying her desk for the evening.

'The tax man.'

Fay snorted. 'I bet that was an interesting journey.'

'It was as it happens. He was able to explain what The Bible & Tract Depot would be exempt from, now the Income Tax Authorities had accepted us as a charitable organisation. I've made a few notes for you....' he rummaged in his jacket pockets bringing out bus tickets, rail tickets, timetables, letters and old invoices.

'Really William. I wish you wouldn't hoard so. I'm sure half the stuff in your pockets is relevant to my books.'

'Yes, they are.' he muttered absently. 'Oh, and there was this.'

'What is it?'

'A letter about me joining up for military duty.'

'What!'

'Apparently my position here doesn't exempt me from National Service.' he said glumly.

'But we couldn't possibly have you leaving as well! The place would

132

fold up!'

William Middleton shrugged. 'It was a bit of a shock I can tell you. But what can I do? It's the....'

'Yes, I know! It's the war!' Fay snapped. She didn't mean to snap but she had had a stressful day. Fay patted his shoulder and said more gently, 'Time to go home William. We'll save the problems of the shop - and the war - for tomorrow and God willing we'll have a night without air raids!'

The shipyards and other industrial installations which crowded along the banks of the Tyne from Newcastle down to the coast were prime targets for the German bombers. Fay had many disturbed and fearful nights as the enemy planes droned high overhead carrying their deadly cargo.

William rose wearily to his feet. He, Olive and their son Billy had a cottage on a farm belonging to Olive's family a few miles out of Newcastle. His mother had not been happy about him living in the country, in case the attractions of farming exceeded those of shopwork in Pilgrim Street. Indeed, William had been tempted on many occasions as he loved the farm, the peace, the quiet and when he could spare the time he would help with harvesting, shooting and general farm work. Even young Billy, his son was taking an active roll, again much to Caroline's displeasure.

But tonight the farm would be a welcome respite from the noise of the city and his hazardous journey to and from London. He would be glad to get home, to his dear wife Olive, Billy and a wholesome hot dinner.

******

The Trustees were horrified when William showed them his papers calling him into National Service full time. There was a general shortage of trained staff, so having just lost two sales assistants and now with the imminent departure of the Manager the Trustees were facing a serious problem. After an exhausting extra-ordinary Trustees meeting, it was finally agreed that William should train Fay to be the acting manageress while he was away and they would do whatever they could to find new staff. What with the publishing industry being in decline, paper rationing and staffing problems, the future business of The Bible & Tract Depot was not looking good.

William thought and prayed deeply over how he could best serve the war effort and as if in answer to his prayers, the authorities decided his age, occupation and general fitness, deemed him more suited for police work in Newcastle. In one stroke of the pen his dilemma over the taking of someone else's life was swept to one side. Being based in Newcastle also gave him the added benefit of being able to keep an eye on Fay as she managed the shop. Many of the able-bodied men from the farm were also being called up and local women had volunteered their services to help with the lambing, harvesting and other general farm duties.

Meanwhile William found that his remaining days at The Bible & Tract Depot were taken up with putting the affairs of the shop in order and showing Fay the duties of a manager. Work began to pile up on her desk as she attempted to learn her new role and serve customers, both upstairs and in the basement. The strain was beginning to tell on them both.

Early one morning the shop door bell tinkled and a cheery voice called, 'Need any help?'

William looked up from the box of books that he was unpacking. and his drawn face broke into a wide smile when he saw John Stephenson and his wife, the former Jane Gibson.

'You two are a welcome sight if you're offering your services!'

Jane's auburn hair was now almost white and she was a little plumper. John Stephenson was standing beside her, and looking younger than a man who had just reached his eightieth birthday. Marriage was obviously good for both of them.

'Mr George Bainbridge told me you were in a pickle.' John said surveying the piles of books waiting to be listed and shelved. So, where would you like us to start?'

'Well...almost anywhere.' William replied, looking around the shop.

Work on the interior had begun just before war had been declared but had not been completed. A lift had been planned to take staff and customers to the offices and landings upstairs, but because of the War, the architect now strongly advised against the it. Consequently a gaping hole had been left in the corner of the shop.

Jane slowly removed her coat and followed his gaze. The book shelves needed dusting, there was a large pile of invoices and papers on Fay Middleton's counter which needed attention and there were boxes of books waiting to be unpacked. Jane had never seen the place look so uncared for. 'It certainly needs attention.' Jane grimaced. 'I can just give you a couple of mornings a week I'm afraid. The hospital have asked me to go in as they are desperate for nursing staff. John can come in a couple of afternoons and...' she chewed at her lip thoughtfully. 'I have a friend who may also be of assistance.'

'We really would appreciate your support.' William said gratefully. 'One or two of the Trustees said they would try to help out too but they have their own businesses to run.'

Jane threw her hands up in mock horror. 'Oh my goodness! Keep *them* away from the shop floor. They might be eminent men but they haven't a clue how to sell a book!'

William laughed.'Hopefully, I will be able to find full-time staff soon.'

The door bell rang and the door opened. A piece of litter drifted in from the street on a warm breeze and the lady, who entered with it, stood framed in the doorway, her dark brown eyes moved slowly over the interior of shop. She seemed uncertain, a little nervous almost, before closing the door behind her. Her navy blue suit emphasised the pallor of her colouring and accentuated her height and slim figure. She looked vaguely familiar to William but he was having difficulty placing a name to the face.

Jane had no such problem. 'Henrietta!' she exclaimed warmly and with her arms outstretched moved over to her friend. 'I'm so pleased you felt well enough to come and help out.' She grasped Henrietta hands. 'Are you all right?' she asked softly.

Henrietta took a deep breath and nodded. 'This is a big step for me Jane.' she whispered. "Are you sure they want me?'

Jane squeezed her friends hand reassuringly then turned to William. 'Mr Middleton, this is Henrietta Harris. Her father worked in the shop with Mr Middleton Senior.'

Henrietta Harris! Of course! William remembered her now. She came with Kate Bainbridge for his father's celebration tea at the shop. She was the one who had had the nervous breakdown. He moved across the floor of the shop with his hand outstretched and a warm smile across his face.

'Miss Harris. I am so grateful for your support. The shop is going through a very difficult period.' He felt as he shook her hand, that if he shook too vigorously, her fingers would fall off. Henrietta Harris smiled back at him.

'I think that I can come in perhaps four days a week Mr Middleton. Is that all right?' she said softly.

'All right? That's marvellous! Thank you so much.'

She came fully into the shop then, the shop that had held so many fears for her as a young girl, walking slowly across the floor, touching the books as if she was coming to terms with all the memories this place held for her. 'When would you like me to start?' she asked.

William waved his arm to display the mess in the shop. 'Well you can see the state we're in. How about...er....now?' He wondered if he was being a bit presumptuous but Henrietta's expression signalled acceptance. 'Now it is then.' she said, as she began to remove her jacket.

Suddenly the shop door bell rang and two customers entered. Jane Gibson glanced at Henrietta nervously but Henrietta, with an air of confidence that surprised even herself, turned to the customers.

'Can I help you?' she asked.

Jane Gibson looked at her husband and John's eyes twinkled in understanding. It was good to be back where they all belonged.

******

April was the time for weddings and William thought he'd never seen his sister, Fay look so radiantly happy as she did on her wedding day. He glanced across to where their mother sat, her lips parted in a half smile. He suspected Fay's marriage to Herbert, like his own marriage to Olive, did not meet wholly with her approval; Herbert was a widowed bank manager with a daughter.

It wasn't a big wedding. The war saw to that but it was such a lovely day and the meal at the hotel was so beautifully set out for them that for probably the first time in their lives, Fay and William forgot all about the shop and, trusting in their skeleton staff, decided to enjoy themselves. In fact Olive threatened, light-heartedly, that if she heard just one word about the shop she'd walk out! Only once did William wonder how the staff were managing, it being Saturday and their busy day, but then he pushed it to the back of his mind and concentrated on his sister's wedding.

Perhaps it was just as well the Middleton family were out of the way. Tom Gibson had been called in to do something with the gaping hole in the corner where the lift shaft had been planned and had decided to arrive that Saturday morning. Jane was annoyed with him.

'You know Saturday is our busy day Tom!' she hissed down the hole. A customer glanced across the shop floor towards them.

136

'Aye! Well y'said anytime, so did Mr Middleton, so I chose today didn't I.'

'You should've know better Tom Gibson. All this banging and your tools lying around untidying the place, it's just not right!'

'My tools don't untidy the place! Anyways the job wouldn't get done without them!'

'You're disturbing the customers and they like to browse."

'I'm not disturbing the customers. I'm down a hole, aren't I?.'

Maggie Russell, the new shop girl listened to the loud exchange between brother and sister with some apprehension but Henrietta Harris just smiled. 'Just like the old times!' she said. The young girl gave Henrietta a watery smile and continued with her task of dusting the shelving.

Maggie Russell wondered how they had coped in the 'old times' if it was always like this. She was a quiet, skinny girl who looked upon William Middleton as God and who flinched when Fay's strict tongue attempted to train her. She much preferred Miss Henrietta Harris who was patient and understanding as she explained the workings of the shop to her.

The floor shook as Tom Gibson hammered a floorboard into place. A customer turned around raising his eyebrows. 'Is that necessary?' he asked.

Jane's face flushed and she was all set to give an angry retort when Henrietta said, 'I'm so sorry sir. I know it's highly unusual, but for the safety of our customers we felt we ought to ask Mr Gibson to come in to sort this problem out as soon as possible. It's the war you know.'

'Hhrruump!' The customer frowned, but nodded, and obviously satisfied with the explanation, bought a book. After he'd left, Jane rested her elbows on the counter of Fay Middleton's desk and surveyed her friend thoughtfully.

'You couldn't have handled something like that at Miss Russell's age.'

'I know.' Henrietta agreed quietly.

Absently, Jane straightened a pile of books. 'How are you coping Henrietta?'

Henrietta watched the three customers browsing around the shelves. 'At one time they would have scared me stiff.' she said honestly. 'But somehow....' she hesitated. 'Having you visiting me when I was in the....the mental hospital all those years ago, letting me talk, accepting me for who I was, did more to aid my recovery than all the pills they shoved down me.'

Jane blushed. 'I wasn't fishing for compliments when I asked that question you know?'

137

'I know, but it's something I've wanted to say for a long time anyway. You've been a good friend to me Jane.' She moved the books to the far end of the counter. 'Did you know the Trustees paid me while I was in hospital, for six months.'

'They did!'

'Yes. That was kind of them. I felt I wasn't just pushed aside because I was...was mentally unstable. They really did care what happened to me.'

'Of course they did. We all did.' Jane patted her friend's arm. 'And I think you better start caring what your trainee is up to. She's just returned the books that gentleman bought, back to the shelves again.'

Henrietta leapt to her feet. 'Oh my goodness! Maggie dear, one moment please.'

Jane's gaze wandered from her friend to the pile of letters and invoices waiting for Fay Middleton's return, or Mrs Fay Watson, as she would now be known. It gave her a good feeling to read about the inner workings of the shop. There was an invoice for seventeen shillings for a fire watcher who was shared with three neighbours in Pilgrim Street. There was a letter from the Newcastle Section of The British & Foreign Bible Society asking if it had any financial responsibilities to the shop in case of damage by enemy action. William had attached a note to the letter and this read:

On examining the Trust Deed it is quite clear there is no such responsibility. Please write and let them know.

Yes it was nice to be back in the shop again knowing that you were doing your bit towards the war effort.

******

William Middleton quite enjoyed his role as policeman during the war. There were always families needing assistance after a bombing raid, people needing information, ambulances, fire engines and traffic to direct. It left him with a sense of being part of restoring lives instead of taking them.

******

The Luftwaffe bombers may have tried to hit The Bible & Tract Depot

- but they missed! As the allies gained a greater footing through Europe and victory became more and more certain, it began to look as if the shop was going to survive the war after all! In 1945 the staff at The Bible & Tract Depot were among the first to decorate their shop window in Pilgrim Street with the red, white and blue of victory!

******

John Stephenson announced that as the shop no longer had any need of his services, he *really was* going to retire this time and enjoy married life to Jane.

******

Henrietta Harris slowly pulled on her gloves on the day of her departure and gazed steadily around the shop floor.

'I'll be leaving now.' she said softly.

Fay lifted her head from her desk and Maggie Russell stopped wrapping books.

'We'll miss you.' Fay said warmly and Henrietta had no doubt she meant what she said. 'You will keep coming in to see us won't you?'

'I'd like that.' said Henrietta Harris. She walked slowly across the shop floor and opened the door. 'Yes.' she said turning her head back to her working colleagues. 'I'd like that very much.' And as she closed the shop door she knew this short time of working in the shop had enabled her to lay her fears to rest - once and for all!

******

So much business had been lost during those war years that William was kept very busy when he returned to his post as manager. He prepared a post war policy for the shop which was warmly welcomed by the Trustees and in the years that followed business slowly began to improve. Paper rationing came to an end and the book trade began to pick up. Grants to The British & Foreign Bible Society, The Colporteur Society and Sunday School Union were duly increased to make up for the loss of revenue during the war years. Families, businesses and industry in general began the long

139

and painful task of re-building.

William's son, Billy was growing into a fine young man, and was showing a greater interest in farming than Caroline, his grandmother, approved of. As William reached his fifties he realised the farm was where Billy's heart lay and he would not be following his father, grandfather, grandmother or Aunt Fay into the work at The Bible & Tract Depot.

Of course telling Caroline, the family matriarch, was quite another matter. Every visit became a battlefield. Even popping in with a few groceries became a skirmish.

'As if one war in a lifetime was not enough!' Olive grumbled as they drove back home to the farm one Saturday morning after a particularly trying visit.

William smiled and steering the car with one hand, gave Olive's fingers a squeeze with the other. Over the years, Olive had shown the patience of a saint with her domineering mother-in-law.

'It's Billy's life and he's free to choose what *he* wants to do with it.' he said vehemently.

'Really? Well I wish you'd be as adamant as that with your mother.'

Releasing Olives fingers he rummaged for his handkerchief and coughed violently into it. The car shuddered.

'Your mother is right about one thing.' Olive added

'What's that?'

'You still haven't fully recovered from that bout of pneumonia.'

'I'm fine. Honestly! I'm just a bit low after being so poorly. All I need is some fresh country air in my lungs to blow away the cobwebs and I'll be fit for work again in a couple of days.'

'Mm'

'In fact I think I might just go shooting. It looks like being a nice afternoon.'

'Mm.'

'Don't keep saying 'Mm' Olive dear. I shall drop you off at the farmhouse then drive up the lane to the far field see if I can't catch that damned fox. Your brother says he's beginning to cost us money!'

'A couple of hours only William. Promise?'

William pulled the old Ford into the farmyard and pulled on the brake. 'Promise dear. A couple of hours and I'll be home.'

Changing quickly into his old trousers, wellingtons and a sweater and donning his cap, he picked up his old sporting gun, some ammunition and headed out of the farmhouse to Olive's shout of, 'A couple of hours only mind William.'

It was one of those crisp autumn days where white clouds sail smoothly across a pale blue sky, blotting out the sun only occasionally but leaving an anticipation for its warm, bright reappearance. William parked his car at the side of the road, then slamming the door wandered over to the gate. Resting his rifle on the gate-post, he leant on the gate and taking a deep breath, gazed across the valley.

There was an earthy smell of freshly ploughed fields standing brown and empty. Bales of hay stood close to the farmhouse in the valley and cattle and sheep grazed in nearby green pastures. It was here he always came after one of his arduous trips to London or when he was worried about the business. Here he was at peace and could see things from a different perspective. Some rooks flew overhead, calling noisily as they reached the trees behind him. He watched them circle then fly towards the stone walling separating the fields. William's eyes lazily scanned the undergrowth nearby. He'd said he was going to look for the fox but it was really just an excuse to have a bit of peace and quiet. His mother could really annoy him at times. Normally he would just agree with her to save an argument then get on with his life as he saw fit but she'd been quite aggressive in her manner this morning and this had annoyed him. Perhaps Olive was right. The after effects of the pneumonia were taking longer to recover from than he imagined. Still he needed to get back to work, and soon! They'd advertised three times now for staff and had been unable to find anyone suitable, which meant they were all having to work extremely hard. His absence hadn't helped either.

His eyes followed the stone walling which lead down to the farmhouse. Repairs were needed in a couple of places and the old barn badly needed the roof seeing to. Perhaps he and Olive's brother could...... A flash of golden brown in the corner of the field caught his eye. The fox! Damned creatures! Foxes killed for the sake of it, leaving their victims a bloodied mess in the fields and the farmer poorer for its existence.

Slowly, so as not to draw attention to himself he picked up his gun while searching in his pockets for some cartridges, before realising that he'd left the ammunition on the passenger seat of the car. Drat! He backed away slowly from the gate. The golden brown creature in the corner of the

141

field never moved. Perhaps it hadn't seen him. Silently he moved towards his car and opening the door slid into the driver's seat with his gun. That fox had better still be there when he got back to the gate. Quickly he pulled the lid off the box of ammunition, picked out two cartridges and pushed one into each barrel. Olive's brother would be delighted if he managed to bag this fox. He glanced out of the window but the hedgerow obscured his view of the fox. Grasping the gun by the barrels he turned to climb out of the car but his wellington boot became lodged under one of the foot pedals. Perhaps it was the unusual angle he twisted to free his foot that caused the gun to discharge one of the barrels. He would never know.

A couple of walkers said they remembered hearing a gun shot and ten minutes later, on reaching the blood-spattered car, they found the body of William Middleton with a large wound in his temple and the gun by his side.

******

The doctor had said that it could have been an accident as there was no sign of violence. But that didn't help Olive or young Billy when the police made enquiries into whether William had any debt worries or whether he had been abnormally depressed; the word "suicide" was mentioned in hushed whispers. The suggestion of suicide distressed Olive greatly. She knew how highly William had held the sanctity of life. He would never, *never* have taken his own! Yet amidst all the gossip, rumours and the resulting painful inquest, her only consolation was the knowledge that the faithful staff of The Bible & Tract Depot would be holding her and Billy in their prayers as they too mourned the death of their manager, William Middleton.

PART FOUR
THE SHOP ON PILGRIM STREET
The Seventies

Fay Middleton walked slowly down Northumberland Street, but then everything she did these days was slow. Old age was catching up with her. It was a cold drizzly depressing November day and Fay Middleton certainly felt depressed. Normally she enjoyed walking down Northumberland Street. It was a more pleasant place to shop in since it was no longer the main A1 route north to Scotland. You never got pushed and shoved by the crowds like you did in the old days. She stopped to gaze into Fenwick's window. Not that she wanted to buy anything but it gave her an excuse to delay entering The Bible House.

Fay Middleton had worked for three years as manageress of The Bible House, following the death of her brother, William. It hadn't been an easy time for her. She had grieved deeply over William. Then came the breakdown of her own marriage. The staff of The Bible House had been so kind and supportive and helped her through those dreadful months. Even after she had retired it had been pleasant to call in to see the staff, sometimes help out behind the counter, but now things had changed.

She left Fenwick's window and crossing over Blackett Street, walked the few yards down Pilgrim Street until she stood outside the shop. Her heart sank. It had never looked so neglected in all the years she had known it. The window display was rather shabby and left a lot to be desired and she sensed that when she walked inside it would not be that warm friendly atmosphere she'd been used to.

The Trustees had asked her to attend an emergency meeting and looking at the state of the window display, she thought that the use of the word "emergency" might be very apt.

She opened the door and entered the shop and after a few brief words with the staff she went upstairs for the meeting.

******

'I did warn you!' Fay Middleton, glared angrily around the room at the five Trustees gathered for that emergency meeting. 'I told you it would be

143

a mistake employing someone to take a more missionary approach. Now Mr. Jacks has taken it up full-time and has left us.' She tapped nervously on the table with her pencil. 'He hadn't a clue how to run the business anyway.' she added.

Mr Albert Peters had been standing staring out of the large arched window overlooking the Odeon cinema. As Fay Middleton finished speaking he turned, the usual humorous twinkle in his eyes were overshadowed by a frown. 'Yes you did warn, Miss Middleton,' he said levelly returning to his seat. The neon lights advertising the new James Bond film, "Diamonds are Forever," flickered annoyingly around the room. 'However, I would remind the meeting that Mr. Jacks was not employed to manage the books or the book-keeping. But now is not the time to be going over old ground. Now is the time to look to the future.'

'What future? The way things stand at the moment, there doesn't appear to be one!' snapped Miss Middleton

'That is a defeatist attitude Miss Middleton!'

Gordon Firth raised his hand in an attempt to stem the growing tension. He was an elderly, upright man, deeply involved in the work of the Baptist Church and other Christian organisations. 'The facts remain that The Bible House is in a financial and staffing crisis. Mr Jacks and our manageress are both extremely distraught.'

'Distraught?' queried Albert Peters.

Gordon Firth stroked his furrowed brow. He could tell he was on the verge of a very bad headache. 'Yes.' he said wearily. 'Mr Jacks pointed out to me, that when he accepted the job in The Bible House, he believed we wanted him to develop a missionary and outreach activity for the business. After two years of building up contacts, he didn't expected to have to drop it all just to return to the shop as book-keeper and replacement for our manageress. He claims it was the stress of the work which has forced him to tender his resignation.'

There was an awkward silence in the room.

'How is Mrs Crawley?' Albert Peters eventually asked

Rowland Hay, the Chairman, shook his head, 'Not at all well when I visited her last week and she was most upset at having to resign as our manageress.'

'Meanwhile who is managing the shop?' another Trustee asked.

'That's the problem.' Gordon Firth answered. 'With no-one at the helm, so to speak, the moral of the staff is severely affected so half of them have left.'

'And goodness knows where he found the present shop girl!' Fay Middleton interjected. 'She always looks so miserable and with her short skirts up to...well, I think she is most unsuitable!'

Mr Hay, gave her a withering glance. 'She was the only one to apply for the post Miss Middleton.'

'What about the H.M.S.O. side of the business?' Rowland Hay asked.

'That's not too healthy either I'm afraid.' Mr Muckle answered. 'The lady who manages it is also very poorly which means we have had two main members of staff absent for some time.' He opened the folder in front of him. 'Shall we have a look at the auditors report in front of us gentleman.'

There was a rustle of paper as all heads bowed to take a look at the current state of affairs and there was silence in the room as they examined at the figures in front of them. They showed quite clearly that their business was in serious decline.

'As you can see gentlemen, our account is at present overdrawn.'

There was a depressed silence around the room. 'Of course the current climate in the publishing market doesn't help matters either.' Albert Peters commented.

'And it does seem to have been getting steadily worse since we changed our name from "The Bible and Tract Depot" to "The Bible House".' another Trustee remarked.

'What are you suggesting?'

'Absolutely nothing! It was just a comment.'

'I thought we agreed that the word "tract" can mislead the general public as to the type of shop...'

'Gentlemen! Gentlemen!' Mr Hay ran his fingers through his hair. 'As I was saying, business is in a bad way. What we have to decide is, can we, with a trading loss of this magnitude, afford to stay open?'

'Not unless we have a miracle.' Albert Peters said softly.

'Not unless we find a new manager.' Gordon Firth added, glancing across at Fay Middleton.

The good lady shook her head. 'I'm far too old and tired to come back to work.' she said firmly.

An uncomfortable silence settled on the meeting. The discussion had focused their minds on the reality of the situation facing them.

'We could reduce our stock and let the first floor premises.'

'Or we could look into the question of letting the whole shop.'

Mr Hay shook his head. 'I don't believe we can do that. Our Trust Deed states quite clearly that The Bible House was founded purely for the sale of bibles and good literature. If we close, I think the property would have to be sold.'

Gordon Firth took a deep breath and all eyes turned in his direction. He had that wonderful ability of being able to come out with just the right thing at just the right time. 'We could ask the Christian Literature Crusade Shop what they would be willing to offer for the stock, should we decide to close.'

Today was one of those days when he didn't come out with just the right thing at just the right time. The trustees looked at each other in despair. Surely it wouldn't come to that! Surely God wasn't drawing this valuable work to a close?

The debate continued until well into the evening. Only once did Albert Peters' glance wistfully across the road towards the Odeon billboards advertising Sean Connery in "Diamonds are Forever", before calling the Trustees and Mrs Middleton to the more important task of praying for God to extricate The Bible House from its financial quagmire.

******

Mrs Edith Quick, was a smart, attractive, lady in her late thirties. Her children were now teenagers and her husband was lecturing at Gateshead College, so she had decided to look for part-time employment for herself. She had found a suitable niche at The Bible House where she filled in for a member of staff, from the H.M.S.O. Department, who had undergone major surgery. She had grasped the work very quickly and had even implemented a few small ideas of her own.

However she was more than amazed when the Trustees called her into the office one morning and offered her the position of manageress of The Bible House. Edith Quick was a level-headed sort of a person, not one to get flustered by such an unexpected request. She paused for a few moments to collect her thoughts before saying, 'That's very kind of you gentlemen, but I feel I have to inform you I've never managed a shop in my life before.'

Gordon Firth nodded his head. 'We know'.

146

'I'm no good at evangelical or outreach work either.'

'We know that too.'

'And I don't know a thing about wages or income tax. In fact I've no training in managing a shop at all!'

'We realise that Mrs Quick,' Gordon Firth said smiling at her. 'Perhaps we ought to explain what you'll be taking on, should you agree to take the post.' He glanced at his colleagues before continuing. 'We are financially in a very bad way. The figures in the ledger don't tie up, the stock is in a mess, the staff.......well, you know all about the staff. Sales are at a very low level and if we don't pay our electricity bill in two weeks, we'll be cut off!' He raised his hands despairingly. 'The bottom line is Mrs Quick, if we don't find someone to get us back on our feet very soon we will be forced to close.'

'Close The Bible House!' Edith Quick was shocked.

'Even as we speak, there are two men from the Christian Literature Crusade shop examining the books and counting the stock, with a view to buying.'

'Does that include the H.M.S.O. department?'

'No. They're not interested in H.M.S.O. That will have to close.'

Edith Quick's heart sank.

Mr Rowland Hay leaned forward on the table. 'We're not expecting you to work miracles Mrs Quick. We recognise your limitations, but what we would like to propose is that for six months, while negotiations are underway with C.L.C., you do what you can to get us back on our feet. It's quite a challenge. Are you willing to take it on?'

Edith Quick took a deep breath and pondered the situation thoughtfully. 'Well,' she said slowly, 'If you are willing to accept my limitations....' the Trustees around the table nodded enthusiastically. 'Then thank you. Yes. It would be a privilege to manage The Bible House.'

Although the future was still rather bleak for The Bible House it was now under new management and there was still hope.

******

'When were these shelves last dusted Janice?'

Janice, the shop girl, the one Fay Middleton described as having a face like a fiddle and short skirt that left little to the imagination, shrugged,

147

'Dunno. The cleaner sometimes used to run a duster over them, but she reckons it's too heavy going for her now and it's not her job anyway, so no one ever bothers. Why?'

'Because I think someone ought to start bothering, don't you?'

Janice crossed her hefty legs and examined the ladder in her stockings. 'Suppose.'

Very carefully she dabbed the brush of her red nail polish on to the top of the ladder and sat back satisfied with her handiwork. She looked over to where her new manageress was checking the book shelves with a duster in her hand.

'The builder was in. Said he'd be in next week to repair the slate what fell off the roof.' she offered.

Edith nodded. Next week would be soon enough. They had to pay the electricity bill first otherwise they would be cut off.

'He also said he'd have a good look at the back of those cupboards what you thought might have damp rot.' Janice allowed some time to elapse before adding, 'And the manager next door wants a word with you about sharing the cost of fire escape doors.'

Edith wrinkled her nose as dust floated down with the handful of books she'd pulled from the top shelf. 'Mm.' was all she said but did not dismiss the question of the fire doors. The Bible House had a skeleton staff, but Edith Quick was very conscious of their safety. She examined the titles of the books in her hand. 'What are these Methodist Local Preacher study books doing among the biographies Janice?'

The girl uncrossed her legs and popped chewing gum into her mouth. 'Dunno.' She chewed for a moment before adding, 'The fire officer rang. Wants you to make an appointment for him to call to discuss fire precautions."

Edith placed the dusty books on the counter before the girl. 'Thank you Janice.' she said levelly. 'It seems I have a lot to do.'

'Aye. Seems like it,'

'So perhaps we can share the work load.'

The gum chewing stopped suddenly. 'Eh?'

Edith Quick handed her the duster. 'You can start by cleaning that side window, the one looking into the narrow lane.'

'But......'

'Mrs Quick.'

148

Edith turned as Mrs Capstaff came down the stairs clattering her mop and bucket against the already chipped and stained walls. She was a small friendly woman who had been cleaner for The Bible House for over twenty years and was already well past retirement age. She stood apologetically before the new manageress.

'I'm right sorry Mrs Quick, I really am, just when you've gone an' got the job of manageress an' I sez to my Arthur, I feel terrible doing this to them but I just have to Mrs Quick. Sorry an all that.'

Edith pushed an unruly curl behind her ear. Her dark brown hair didn't usually get unruly, in fact very little became unruly with Edith Quick, but this morning seemed to be an exception. 'Do what to us Mrs Capstaff?' she asked patiently.

'Well it's like this see. I've done this shop for more than twenty-two years and it's just gettin' too much see, so me and Arthur felt I ought to be thinking of handing in my notice. Of course I realise it's a difficult time what with......' Her voice tailed off and her eyes drifted from Edith Quick's face as something caught her attention behind the manageress. The shadow of a large vehicle suddenly blotted out the light from the window overlooking the narrow lane at the side of the shop. 'That there lorry is never gonna ....' Her eyes suddenly widened, there was a cry of alarm from Janice, and Edith Quick turned, just in tme to see the lorry shatter the window, sending glass flying across the floor.

There was a stunned silence in the shop, which fortunately was free of customers at the time. A very shaken lorry driver squeezed out of his cab and poked his head through the gaping hole in the window, and offered his apologies.

Janice turned to Edith Quick, and with only a trace of sarcasm said, 'Guess I won't have to clean that window now eh?'

******

Harry Hopkins, or "Hoppy" as he was generally known around the streets of Newcastle, stood peering through the window of The Bible House, his fingerless gloves clutching a paper bag containing his pasty. He shivered, turned up the collar of his old army coat and pulled his wool hat further over his ears. It was a cold afternoon. Christmas shoppers thronged Northumberland Street, gazing in awe at the Christmas scenes in Fenwick's

149

window. The colourful lights decorating the town swung gently in the wintry breeze and from somewhere came the strains of a carol, reminding passers-by of the Christmas message. In general, Christmas didn't mean very much to Hoppy. All the shops were closed over the holiday and he was forced to stay in his one room by himself. He didn't like that as he preferred to be in the town with the shops open, which brought people into the City Centre in droves. He sniffed, rubbing his shabby coat sleeve across his nose, then touched his pasty - it was cold. Bainbridge's in Market Street used to give him the occasional hot pasty and cup of tea, but now that the store was owned by the John Lewis Partnership, things had changed. Fortunately other bakeries in the area would often sneak the odd pasty into his hands. The trouble was, Hoppy liked his pasty hot and the central heating pipes in the basement of The Bible House, made an ideal oven. But Hoppy always asked first. He never took it for granted that he would be allowed inside. After all, he was an alcoholic and a bit weird in the head - so he was told!

Plucking up his courage he entered The Bible House with the jangle of the door-bell alerting the staff to his entrance. Both Edith Quick and Janice glanced up to see Hoppy, in his oversize boots, shuffle over to the counter at the back of the shop where Edith Quick sat.

She was looking at the sheet of paper in her hand as if she hoped it might just suddenly disappear into thin air and she wouldn't have to worry about it any more. It hadn't been any easy start for Edith Quick. In fact it had been hard work familiarising herself with wages, tax, bank statements. account ledgers, sales, invoices and stock. The fact that she now had a broken window, suspected damp rot, pressure from the fire officer to fulfil the fire regulations, urgent bills to pay, no cleaner, a staff shortage and a clueless shop girl, only added to her problems.

Distracted from her bills and invoices, Edith waited for Hoppy to reach the counter. 'Hello Hoppy - can I help you?.' she inquired.

'I've come to warm me pasty.' Hoppy stood awkwardly before her.

'Yes. that's all right. You know where to go.'

She dropped her eyes to look at the papers in her hands while Hoppy continued to stare at her. She looked tired, he thought, but that was only to be expected. He's seen the lights on in the shop until late in the evening every night for weeks now. When he had peered through the window he had seen her working, pouring over the books and ledgers, just like now.

Hoppy lowered his head and shuffled towards the basement.

The door-bell signalled another arrival, this time it was a customer. Inquistive as ever, Hoppy paused on the landing leading to the basement. The customer was a thin, middle-aged woman with a pale, distraught face. Hoppy stood silently by the basement door watching her. She hovered around the shelving which held the Bibles, but even Hoppy sensed that she wasn't really looking at them. People often came into The Bible House, not looking for books but for help with personal problems. That daft Janice, the one with the short skirts and big legs, just ignored the woman, but Mrs Quick, moved from behind the counter, and approached the woman. That was what Hoppy liked about Mrs Quick. No matter how busy she was, she still had time for you.

'Can I help you?' she said, with a smile on her face.

'I er...' The woman appeared agitated and a little lost for words.

'Are you all right?'

'Yes...I...no...' The woman then burst into tears. 'I'm sorry, it's just....'

'Come and sit down for a moment.' Mrs Quick guided her over to a chair by the counter.

Hoppy suddenly remembered the pasty he was supposed to be heating. Ah, well. It could wait. He was suddenly more interested in what was happening in the shop. Hoppy went down two stairs, until he was out of sight and then he stopped, turned and peered round the corner to listen to what Mrs. Quick was saying. However, it was the woman who seemed to be doing most of the talking.

The woman was explaining, between sobs, about losing her husband. Friends and relatives were very kind but she was finding it very difficult to adjust to her loss. She was lonely and wondered about talking to a vicar. Hoppy sniffed and wiped the sleeve of his coat across his nose again. He didn't know much about losing anybody as he'd never had anyone to lose in the first place, but he could understand what the woman meant when she talked about being lonely. Ah! Now that was something he knew about! As for needing a vicar? The only time Hoppy would need a vicar was for his funeral. He would like some nice words to be said about him when his time came. Otherwise he had no time for the church, unless it came in the form of Salvation Army handouts or a meal.

Hoppy watched as Mrs Quick made a phone call.

'Hello? S.P.C.K.?' Hoppy knew that was another Christian book shop in the city. He didn't go there very often as it didn't have hot pipes for his pasty or a picture of the Queen in the basement. He liked the Queen. He *loved* the Queen!

'I have a lady with me who is in need of a minister. (pause) You have? That's excellent. (pause) He'll be with us in ten minutes. Thank you.'

As she replaced the receiver Edith Quick noticed Hoppy peering from the basement stairway.

'Janice, would you take Hoppy down to the basement, please?'

Janice grimaced but without argument moved towards him. Hoppy turned and, hastily, thumped his way down the stairs to the basement with his pasty - saving Janice the bother of ushering him downstairs

The colourful Christmas lights strewn across Northumberland Street, flickered into life late in the afternoon, but Edith Quick barely noticed them when she glanced out of the window. Somehow she didn't feel part of the Christmas celebrations this year. As she waited for the minister to arrive from S.P.C.K., her own problems surfaced in her mind. Besides which, she didn't feel at all well. She was tired, her head ached and there was a gnawing in her stomach where her lunch should have been.

Meanwhile, Hoppy had placed his pasty on the hot water pipes and then decided to have another look upstairs while he waited for his pasty to warm up. Moving as quietly as his boots would allow he arrived at the top and peered into the shop.

The vicar and the woman were just being shown out of the door by Mrs Quick. He was pleased about that. Whenever anyone in trouble came into the shop, there was always someone they could send them to. Just as they were leaving Mrs Quick held open the door to allow a young lady to enter. Hoppy thought she looked nice. Brown curly hair fell softly across her face and when she spotted him peering around the corner her smile was wide and friendly, but he didn't smile back. Safer that way!

At that moment Janice also noticed that Hoppy had arrived back in the shop. She stopped her shelving work and glared at him. Hoppy turned tail and off he went downstairs again, this time followed by an irritated Janice, moving as fast as her short tight skirt and high-heels allowed.

The girl turned to Mrs Quick, 'The minister at our church said you were looking for staff.' The girl had a quiet gentle voice and she shuffled her feet uncertainly.

'Please come over here and sit down.' Edith indicated the chair at the side of the counter and they exchanged pleasantries for a few moments before Edith said, 'Tell me a little bit about yourself.'

'Well, I'm er......' The girl was about to launch into her story when the sound of raised voices drifted up from the basement.

Edith rose from her chair. 'Excuse me please. I won't be a moment.' She went over to the top of the stairs, listened and then shouted. 'Janice! Janice appeared at the bottom of the stairs. 'Look Janice, unless he is disturbing any customers down there, just let Hoppy talk to the Queen as usual!'

'But he's crackers Mrs Quick! He's weird.'

'He's harmless Janice!'

'Harmless? You call that racket harmless?'

From behind her came a loud pitiful wail. 'I know I've been a bad boy y'majesty! I know I have but y'majesty....'

'He's kneeling in front of the Queen's picture talking to her!' explained Janice.

Mrs Quick's visitor wondered if she had enough time to sneak out of the shop before Mrs Quick returned. The place was a mad house! What was she doing applying for a job here?

The exchanges between manageress and shop girl came to an abrupt end

'I'm sorry about that.' said Edith Quick, apologetically, as she returned to her seat. 'We have a picture of the Queen in our H.M.S.O. Department downstairs and Hoppy, our er.... occasional but eccentic visitor, likes to talk to her while he heats his meat pie on the hot water pipes.' Edith Quick stopped talking. Her explanation of the situation sounded ludicrous even to herself! Goodness knows what the young lady made of it.

'Now!' she said struggling to maintain some form of professional efficiency. 'Tell me a little bit about yourself.'

There wasn't an awful lot to tell but Edith heard only half the story anyway. If the truth of the matter be known, she was feeling slightly light-headed, perhaps from the lack of food coupled with the stresses of the day, and so she heard only of the girl's desire to work part-time.

'Part time?' Edith repeated. 'I'm sorry, I should have said sooner. We're really after a full-time worker.'

'Oh.' The girl looked a little despondent.

A wail came from the basement. 'Forgive me y'majesty. Forgive me!

I'll be a good boy over Christmas.'

Ignoring the lamentations from the basement, Mrs Quick said, 'Unless....'

'Yes?' The girl's hang dog expression lifted expectantly.

'Unless you help us out with full-time work until Christmas and.....' Mrs Quick's offer was interrupted by another outburst from Hoppy.

'Howay man! What've you dun to me pasty y'stupid ... It's still cold!' came the angry voice of Hoppy.

The girl glanced towards the basement stairway. 'Well.....' she hesitated.

Janice's high pitched voice rang up the stairs. 'You're a dirty old.....'

Edith Quick coughed loudly. Such language! And in The Bible House! 'We are in need of full time staff.' she said. 'The pay is....'

'The pay?'

Edith looked at the girl's puzzled expression. 'What's wrong?'

'I thought this was voluntary work. You mean you'll pay me?'

Edith suppressed the bubble of laughter that threatened to rise to the surface. She really was feeling very light-headed. 'Yes, we er...we do normally pay our staff.' she explained.

The girl's expression lightened. 'Well I could work full-time, over the busy period and then, perhaps, three days a week. Would that be of use to you?'

Edith Quick didn't have any hesitation in accepting the offer. 'That would be wonderful.' she said. She knew she wasn't employing her out of desperation. She had liked the girl immediately and she had a very definite hunch that she would prove to be more than suitable. 'When can you start?'

The girl glanced uncertainly towards the basement stairway. 'Er...anytime. Monday?'

Edith Quick stood up and reached out her hand. 'Then Monday it is.'

The girl stood up just as Janice pattered up the stairs from the basement. 'He's a blinkin' loony!' she spat vehemently. 'He blames me 'cos his pasty fell behind the pipes!'

Edith Quick, anxious not to give the wrong impression sent a warning shot with her eyes towards Janice. 'We will have a new member of staff joining us on Monday Janice.' she said, changing the subject.

'Oh good.' said Janice without any real enthusiasm, as she eyed the girl up and down and then fixed her gaze on the girl's shoes.

'I was hoping you wouldn't notice.' the girl said in an embarrassed manner, as she turned and hurried out of the shop door. It was only then that Edith noticed that the new employee was wearing odd shoes.

Mrs Quick sat down in her chair and gave way to the laughter which had threatened to overwhelm her. Yes, the new girl would fit very nicely into this shop. Very nicely indeed!

Down in the basement Hoppy had retrieved his dusty, but warm pasty, from behind the hot water pipes and bid a farewell to his Queen, 'I'll be back soon your majesty!' he promised. He turned and clumped his way upstairs - satisfied!

******

No-one quite knew how she did it. In fact looking back, Edith Quick couldn't quite work out how she did it herself! But within six months, she was beginning to see daylight through the sheaves of overdue invoices and demand letters. After contacting most of their big publishers and explaining their present position, she was relieved to discover they were quite amenable to waiting for payment. By the end of June the entries in the account book began turning from red to black and the Trustees of The Bible House were relieved to inform The Christian Literature Crusade Shop, that they would not be selling their stock after all!

Edith Quick would have been the first one to admit that she didn't do it all by herself, but she did take the credit for employing a team of efficient staff - with the exception of Janice. Janice had, in fact, decided that selling books was not her forte and that she was far better suited to selling fashion clothes, so she left. Edith Quick's predecessor had fortunately returned to her old position selling H.M.S.O. stock in the basement. As business began to grow under an efficient manageress, other part-time workers were able to be employed.

There was only one mistake Edith Quick felt she had made and that was employing a French student from Newcastle University, as their cleaner. Unfortunately Marguerite was more concerned with improving her English than cleaning the shop and incessantly practised her very bad English on anyone who would listen. She had this strange notion that all the English were concerned about was the weather, so before the staff of The Bible House could start work every morning they were subjected to a full scale weather report from Marguerite.

'Ah! The weather. Eet ees waining this morning, no?'

'Yes Marguerite.' The staff would answer patiently. 'It is waining...er raining.'

'But it will sunshine this next morning, no?'

'No, I mean yes. Er, yes. Tomorrow it will.... Aren't you supposed to be cleaning the basement this morning Marguerite?'

'The basement? Ah! Down the steps yes? No fresh air in the er...basement no?'

It was only after the girl had gone that one of the staff remarked, 'I wish she'd learn something new to say about the weather other than "It is waining" or "it is sun shining". If we had a heat wave, that would be a new one for her.'

'In November?'

'Poor girl. I think we should make it our goal for the next few months to help her with her English.'

A few days later Marguerite arrived into work late. She'd been studying until well into the night and had slept in. As she hurried into the shop there were already a few customers who were shopping early for Christmas.

'Ah, good day to you.' Marguerite exclaimed loudly as she burst into the shop. 'I am so sorry I am not here.'

The customers looked up and smiled at the bright little French girl with such a quaint accent and the staff smiled and waited patiently for their daily forecast.

'The weather today,' said Marguerite rubbing her hands to warm them up. 'Ah the weather today, it is.....*craps*!'

There was a shocked silence around the shop floor from customers and staff alike. They all stood and looked at Marguerite. The girl winced. 'I say something wrong?'

There was a snigger from a Sunday School teacher behind one of the shelves.

'*Crisp*! Marguerite. I think you mean that the weather is *crisp*!'

Eventually, Marguerite left having graduated in something or other, but thanks to the staff of The Bible House, it certainly wasn't in English!

******

Mrs Quick was delighted to receive a reply to her advertisement for tenants to rent rooms on the top floor. Or rather she was delighted with the rent that Tyneside Youth For Christ would be paying. The only item the room lacked was a telephone.

'No problem.' Edith answered. 'I shall have one installed for you.'

Unfortunately it turned out to be more of a problem than they had anticipated. The council decide to do a few road repairs on the same morning that the telephone engineer came to install the new line, shattering the quiet book room with the hammering of their pneumatic drill. Then the telephone engineer himself turned out to be a most uncooperative chap. With little or no warning he switched off the telephone lines to The Bible House while he installed the new line for Tyneside Youth for Christ. Edith Quick was most upset! She stood towering over him at the open door of The Bible House while he knelt on the ground fiddling with a fistful of wires.

'This *is* a shop.' she informed him politely. 'I hope we will be on line again very soon otherwise we will be losing orders.'

'Eh?'

Edith Quick glared at the men dancing with their pneumatic drill directly outside her shop. 'I said, I hope we will be on line again soon otherwise we will be losing orders!' she shouted. 'Will you be long?'

The man shook his head. 'No, not long!' he shouted back. 'But I've fixed up that other line now. Why don't you use that?'

'The other line?'

'Yes Missus! The one for the top floor.'

Edith shook her head and glared at the road workers again. 'That's for Tyneside Youth for Christ!' she bellowed.

The man looked at her blankly for a moment then shrugged his shoulders. 'That's all right. I'm sure he'll not mind you using *his* line!'

This time Edith looked blankly at the engineer then slowly it dawned. 'No!" she shouted. I said, *that's for Tyneside Youth for......*' Then, shaking her head in despair, she gave up. There really were times when she wondered if the Almighty kept this place for His own amusement!

******

The Bible House profits were now increasing, so the annual donations to The Sunday School Union and The Bible Society, also increased accordingly. Unfortunately the shop did hit a worrying patch at the end of the second year when the country was faced with one of its most acrimonious industrial disputes. As oil from the Middle East, natural gas from the North Sea and nuclear energy became more popular, there was a reduced demand for coal from the nationalised mining industry. The miners were dissatisfied. Their working conditions were bad, their pay was low and they were determined to challenge Prime Minister Ted Heath and his Conservative Government on the question of pay, they went on strike. Many believed this would be a short strike but there was a strong political element in it and as violent clashes between pickets and the police became more frequent, it became evident that the government would have to act.

Although the coal industry was much less important to the north-east than it had been in the past, there was a lot of sympathy in the area for the miners and their families. However, as the strike intensified, the coal stocks at power stations dwindled and rolling power cuts reduced the whole of the country to periods of three days per week to conserve coal stocks. The miners' and their strike became a topic of heated discussion.

As usual, The Bible House played its part in conserving coal by placing lamps on the counter and around the shelves. No-one grumbled because everyone was in the same position and as Betty, one of the part-timers remarked late one afternoon, when the lamps cast strange shadows around the walls and bookshelves, 'It's cosy isn't it? It gives you a feel of what the place must have been like years ago when they were reliant on gas lamps.'

'And on coal fires to warm the place.' Sandra, another member of staff agreed. 'I'm glad I didn't have to carry buckets of coal up all those stairs.' She frowned. 'Do you think we might get laid off if the three-day week goes on much longer?'

Betty smiled at her colleagues concerned face. 'Don't worry,' she said. 'Mrs Quick won't let that happen.'

'Mm,' Sandra sounded uncertain. "I don't think even Mrs Quick could sort the mining industry out!'

Betty chuckled. 'After what she's done to this place I wouldn't be too ....' She was cut short by a cry of alarm from the basement. Startled, the two ladies hurried to the back of the shop and were halfway down the stairs, their eyes peering through the semi-darkness in the basement, when they saw water pouring through the fire escape door and their colleague rushing around in the gloom trying to lift boxes and books off the lower shelves.

'Hurry! Get Mrs Quick!' Betty ordered.

Sandra rushed off up the stairs and with only a slight hesitation, Betty stepped on to the saturated carpet to help.

'We better remove those law books off that lower shelf!' she said grabbing a handful. Icy cold water splashed on to the back of her legs as she bend down. 'Where do you think it's it coming from?'

The woman piled the books one on top of each other. 'No idea. It was just a trickle through the door a few minutes ago, then all of a sudden there was a gush of water and it began pouring through. I think there must be a burst water main somewhere on Pilgrim Street.' She carried them over to the counter. 'Oh, thank goodness! Here's Mrs Quick.'

Edith Quick, took a deep breath when she saw the state of her basement. 'How long has it been like this?' she asked sharply.

Betty took off her shoes and put them on the chair behind the counter. 'Not long. Only a few minutes,' she answered hurrying back to the shelves. 'But the water has already reached the far wall.'

'And it's beginning to rise.' Sandra added worriedly.

Edith hurried back up the stairs and calmly, so as not to alarm the customers, instructed her staff to call the Water Board, then organise for one member of staff to be left on each floor and the rest to help in the basement.

Within minutes, the manageress and staff of The Bible House had discarded their shoes and were wading ankle deep around the gloomy basement in icy cold water, lifting books and H.M.S.O. stock from the lower shelves to the higher ones. They didn't speak unless it was to warn or give instruction. To have their precious H.M.S.O. stock damaged was unthinkable!

As they worked, they surveyed the rising water in alarm. Before long it had risen almost up to their knees and was lapping around their skirts. Undaunted, the ladies of The Bible House lifted their skirts and with as much speed as they could muster, considering they were wading through freezing cold water and in the gloom, continued lifting the stock above water level.

They were really starting to get alarmed when a very welcome squad from the Water Board arrived and informed them the burst pipe had been located by their colleagues on Pilgrim Street, and the water should soon begin to subside.

Edith suddenly felt exhausted and leaning on the counter to survey the mess. Other than a solitary sheet of paper bobbing around on the water, all of the H.M.S.O. stock had been saved. Books, files and stationery were piled in a disorderly fashion on every available surface above water level, including the stairs. She turned to her wet and dishevelled staff, slumped against the counter and on chairs in a state of exhaustion and was overcome with a sense of pride in them.

'I think we have done a very good job here, ladies.' she said smiling at them. 'Now, out of the water all of you and up to the staff room to dry out and have a hot drink. Then off home you go. I don't want any of you going down with colds.'

They didn't argue. They were too exhausted to argue. Besides which, they knew there was nothing more they could do until the water had been drained off. It sloshed as they waded wearily across the floor.

It was only as her staff staggered up the stairs with the edges of their skirts dripping water, that Edith Quick felt the first stabbing pain in her hip. 'It's standing around in that cold water,' she told herself. 'Nothing more.' Firmly she pushed the discomfort out of her mind. She had no time for aches and pains. There was far too much work to be done!

******

The miners' strike ended in a humiliating defeat for the Government and the pits got back into production again. With mixed opinions over the strike, the country returned to a full working week and with great relief the public felt the benefits of electricity, lighting and heating their homes and offices once more.

Of course it took a long time for the stone floor and the carpet to dry out after the flood in the basement and a rather unpleasant smell lingered for a number of weeks. Even Hoppy found it necessary to complain when he arrived to heat his pasty.

'Yer basement stinks Mrs!' he rasped, standing at the top of the basement stairs.

'Be quiet Hoppy.' Edith reprimanded in a low voice. 'You don't want to scare our customers away do you?'

The man shrugged and examined his pasty more closely, dropping crumbs on the carpet as he did so. 'It's unhygienic doon here. That's what it is!'

'It's quite clean I assure you. Just heat your pie then go.' she said

'Aye, well I might need to complain to the social services.' he warned.

'You do that!'

Hoppy droned on. '"Nobody'll want to go doon there. It stinks!' He paused, waiting for someone to argue with him. He was in the mood for a good argument. Unfortunately for him no one else was. Then his mood changed suddenly and he dropped his eyes to his boots. 'Can I er...can I have some of me money?' he muttered.

Some months ago, during one of his more sober periods, he had asked Mrs Quick if she would look after his Social Security money each week, in an attempt to avoid spending it all on drink. Then each morning he presented himself at the counter for enough cash to buy his dinner.

'I gave you your money this morning Hoppy.'

'Aye, but I need more. The strike's affected the cost of living,' he said plaintively.

Fortunately another member of staff came to the rescue. 'Come on, Hoppy,' she said breezily. 'Get yourself downstairs to heat your pasty before we have too many customers. I know there's a horrible damp smell down there but the smell of your after-shave will soon dispel it.'

Hoppy beamed at her. 'Aye it will that.' he said easily pacified, then wandered down to the basement with her, delighted to be of service to The Bible House.

******

There were only two major changes that Hoppy did not approve of. One was Mr. Ridley. Mr Ridley was a reasonably well-dressed, middle-aged man who began coming into the shop to use the telephone. He would ring his vicar, Social Services, the newspaper, police, fire services and in fact anyone who would listen. Hoppy could hardly believe the cheek of the man. He reckoned Mr Ridley was even dafter in the head than himself!

The staff watched Mr Ridley warily at first, then began glancing at each other with some amusement every time he came in. Hoppy wondered why they didn't just give him a flea in his ear, but then they weren't like that. Anybody, absolutely anybody, could walk into The Bible House - and they didn't have to buy a book!

161

He had watched a young man who had been comforted by one of the staff upstairs, heading for the "Listening Post", run by Brunswick Methodist Church, just a few minutes walk away. 'Why don't you send *him* there?' He nodded his head in the direction of Mr Ridley who appeared to be having a long and detailed discussion with a member of the clergy.

'He does all his talking on our telephone, that's why.' Anyway, he's just lonely.'

'So am I!' Hoppy complained. 'But I divvint spend all me time chattin' on the phone!'

Eventually, Mr Ridley had to be asked by the staff not to use the telephone quite so much as it was running a bit expensive.

The man bristled. 'I've never heard such nonsense in all my life!' he said haughtily and marched out of the shop.

They thought they'd seen the last of him, but some weeks later he turned up again and the whole procedure started all over again. Mr Ridley, it seems, was, like Hoppy, one of the "resident" visitors to The Bible House.

The other major change that upset both Hoppy and Mr Ridley, was the refurbishment which took place in the shop. There was a lot of standing around by the Trustees, shaking their heads or nodding them in approval, looking first at the basement and then the shop front. The architect and the builder would arrive and a deal of hand waving ensued as they described how the finished result would look. Finally, there was a lot of running around by the staff, as they moved the stock from floor-to-floor while the builders were busy, then moved it back again after they had finished.

The staff were delighted with their new working conditions - or at least they would be when they'd recovered from their exhaustion. Mrs Quick, was very pleased, very pleased indeed with her new shop but slightly disturbed by the pain in her hip every time she walked up and down the stairs. The Trustees were very pleased with the new look given to The Bible House - but Hoppy was devastated! They had changed the pipes which he used for heating his pasty!

The shop front had a large new modern window, completely altering its appearance from the outside. The basement containing H.M.S.O. publications had been modernised and the children's department on the first floor was given a lift as well.

Of course paying for all this was quite another matter. Hoppy heard the Trustees talking about it being a "step of faith", whatever that was. Hoppy didn't have faith in anybody except himself. Although...did he? When his fuddled brain allowed him to, he pondered this point and came to the conclusion that he did have faith. Faith in the folk of The Bible House. They had handed out his Social Security money to him for years to help him stay off the drink - and it had worked - mainly. Yes, he did have faith. Faith in them and.....and....Hoppy screwed his face up. It was hard work thinking. If he had faith in them, and they had faith in God, then...then... then a vicar was sure to say nice things over his grave when his time came, wasn't he? Anyway! Faith or no faith, he still didn't like the new shop!

The 1990s

If she had been asked where the years had gone, Edith Quick would have been hard pushed to tell you. Twenty seven years on and to Mrs Quick's credit, The Bible House had grown once more into a thriving concern. The Trustees were more relaxed and the staff were happy. Unfortunately, advancing years have a habit of accentuating irritating problems and Edith Quick became irritated by the growing discomfort in her hip.

Forced to take a couple of hours off work to visit the doctor, and that in itself was an irritant as she was never off work, she sat in his surgery waiting for the verdict. Edith was told she would require an operation. Somehow she had expected this verdict and in one way she was relieved to know what the problem was. But on the other hand she worried about being able to handle all those stairs in The Bible House. Of course the staff noticed, they were bound to, but when asked if she was in pain she would just reply cheerfully, "Just a little stiff today, that's all." Normally a very truthful person, this deception upset her greatly and she knew sooner or later she would have to address the problem.

The problem was addressed sooner rather than later. The Trustees rarely visited on Tuesdays, so it was completely out of the normal routine when Mr David Kilner, walked into the shop. Edith Quick raised her eyebrows in surprise.

'Good morning Mr Kilner.'

Mr David Kilner was a brisk efficient accountant with a jovial manner that endeared him to Mrs Quick, for he was never too rushed to stop and listen to the daily ups and downs of The Bible House, or to share a joke with her.

'Good morning Mrs Quick,' he said easily. 'Are you busy?'

She glanced down at the ledger in front of her. 'No. This can wait. Can I help you?' He stood for a moment, slightly uncertain, then asked, 'How are you recovering from the major refurbishment we've had done to the place?'

'The staff are ....'

'No, I mean you personally Mrs Quick. I wondered if, with all the running around you've had to do, you were finding the stairs a bit of a problem?'

She felt her stomach lurch. 'No,' she replied cheerfully clocking up another lie. 'Not too bad.' She bit her lip under his steady gaze. 'Sometimes I do find it a bit er..tiring.' she added.

He nodded understandingly then stood back, waiting patiently while she served a customer.

'Do you feel up to coming on a tour of the shop with me.' he asked after the customer had left.

She looked up at him with a puzzled frown. 'Yes, of course,' she answered then turning to Betty, one of her staff, said 'Could you take over for me here at the counter for a while please Mrs Richmond?'

She was glad he was ahead of her as they made their way down the stairs into the basement. She would have hated him to see how difficult she found the stairs. He led her to the back of the shop, where the Health and Safety books were on display and out of earshot of the staff behind the counter.

'What do you see?' he asked softly.

'Pardon?'

'What do you see on this shop floor?' he repeated.

She looked around slightly bemused. 'Well, the new carpet has made a difference and er...that basement smell has gone.'

'Anything else?'

'Well - the staff have made an excellent job of displaying the books around the top shelves. The place looks quite cheerful doesn't it?'

'Mm.' A comfortable silence settled between them before he asked, 'Do you remember those days when it was just lit with a couple of light bulbs and there was a warm dank smell?'

Edith smiled. 'And we had to climb steps to use the little sink in the back room.'

'And there was a howling gale down those stairs from the back door.' David Kilner waved his arm around the basement. 'Now look at it.' he said softly.' Look at what you created.'

'Ah, but the staff....'

'Yes they have played their part in making it successful but *you* were the one who enabled The Bible House to survive through its most difficult period.'

She lowered her eyes, embarrassed by the unexpected praise. He wandered over to the foot of the stairs. 'Come with me.' he said.

She followed him slowly up the stairs and stood beside him while he surveyed the shelves at the back of the shop.

'Are you looking for anything in particular?' she asked puzzled.

'I was just wondering if we could set up an office, either in the basement or at the back of the shop here for you?' he said without looking down at her.

Edith Quick could feel herself filling up with tears. She shook her head. 'I know what you're trying to do.' she said softly. 'And it won't work.'

David Kilner straightened one of the books on the shelf. 'And what am I trying to do Mrs Quick?'

Edith lifted her head to face him, fighting back the tears. 'A manageress needs to be able to visit every floor of her shop.' she said shakily. 'And I....I can't do that as...as well as I used to. My mobility has become...somewhat limited Mr Kilner.'

Mr. Kilner nodded sadly. 'But we can still come to some arrangement. We don't want to lose you Mrs Quick. You have been, and still are, far too valuable to us. Perhaps you could spend more time on the paperwork, working from the ground floor.'

She shook her head again. 'And do you really think I would be satisfied doing half a job after the amount of work I've put into this place?' she asked softly.

David Kilner hesitated. 'No,' he said thoughtfully. 'I don't think you would.'

Edith didn't answer.

In some ways she was grateful for that conversation with Mr Kilner. It enabled her to come to the decision to retire. Edith Quick was of the opinion that if you had a job to do, you either did it well or not at all and it had troubled her that her deteriorating health had become an obstacle to her doing her job well, but she did worry about the future of The Bible House and her staff. Would her successor be able to spend the long hours necessary on the accounts if The Bible House was in trouble, like she had done? Would they be able to build up a good team of staff behind them? What would happen if they let the place fall into decline after all her hard work?

******

The prospective new manageress was introduced to her by one of the Trustees, Mr Albert Peters. He stood hovering around, anxious for the two ladies to like each other.

'Hello. I'm Beryl Johnson.' She was a quietly spoken woman in her early forties in a smart pale grey suit. Straight brown hair framed a round, pleasant, smiling face and blue eyes crinkled through her spectacles in a genuine greeting. She was a Christian, a Methodist, married to a bank manager and had two teenage sons. Her husband and Mr Peters, in fact, knew each other from their involvement in the Boys' Brigade.

Edith Quick, rather slowly and painfully, stood up from her desk as the woman reached out her hand in greeting. 'I am delighted to meet you, Mrs Johnson.' Edith said.

By the end of her second week of training, Edith had to admit Beryl Johnson was a quick learner and not afraid to ask questions. She also had a few good ideas of her own, which Edith recognised were quite feasible, and she also had expertise in other fields. Edith was left with the feeling that Mrs Johnson might just be the right person to take up the reins of managing The Bible House after all.

The staff insisted on giving Mrs Quick a farewell party. It was a grand affair with gifts, food and drinks, speeches and invitations to visit. Edith was glad of the invitations. Her husband had died recently so there would be no companion to spend her retirement with and she'd put so much of her life into the shop that she'd never had much time for hobbies. There was a presentation by the Trustees in gratitude for her long and devoted service and then suddenly it was all over.

Her last day of working at The Bible House, dawned bright and clear but as she opened up the shop, Edith was struggling with an assortment of emotions and the staff were subdued and quiet. Almost as if she sensed the

166

deep sadness in the shop, Beryl Johnson deferred to Edith, quietly serving customers in the different departments as though she was an employee and not the new manageress of The Bible House. Edith was grateful for her sensitivity. Many long-standing customers called in or sent cards of greeting. It was quite overwhelming and, not being one for expressing deep emotions, Edith struggled to keep the tears at bay all day.

She knew it would be difficult at five o'clock. Not only would the staff want to say their final good-byes but she would have to hand over the keys to Mrs Johnson and she would be the one set the burglar alarm and to lock the door. Edith slowly took her coat from behind the counter and started putting it on.

'We're going to miss you Mrs Quick. We really are,' Betty said and her face crumpled. 'I'm not going to cry! I'm not! But you must come in to see us.'

Edith couldn't stop the tears coming into her eyes. 'I don't think so dear.' she said rapidly blinking them away. 'It wouldn't be fair to your new manageress.'

Betty blew her nose noisily then pushing her paper handkerchief up her sleeve suddenly threw her arms around her. 'Then you'll have to come to visit me. I mean it!'

Edith nodded. She couldn't trust herself to speak.

One by one they left, these people who had been her staff for so many years and had helped her build this shop into what it was today. She stood at the door and watched them go, then she took a final look around her Bible House.

They had a great big picture window looking on to Pilgrim Street these days and the window display was always bright and beautifully set out. Edith always insisted on it being changed regularly. The counter with its new modern till was set in the corner by the shop door and there were racks of cards for all occasions to greet those who entered the shop.

This was it then! She was actually leaving. Her eyes lighted on Beryl Johnson, standing discreetly at the back of the shop with her coat on, sensitively waiting, with the keys in her hands, to lock up the shop. Their eyes met and held in some form of mutual understanding. Neither spoke. Then Edith took a deep breath.

'I hope all goes well with you Mrs Johnson,' she said.

Beryl smiled and it was as if the whole of the shop smiled with her, for it had heard similar words of blessing from one manageress to another over one hundred and twenty years ago, when Miss Margaret Wilson, had handed over the management to Miss Elisabeth Smith.

The new manageress smiled, her slow pleasant smile and replied as Miss Elisabeth Smith had done. 'Thank you Mrs Quick.' she said gently. 'Be assured it will. It will!'

The 21st Century

The Bible House was moving into the 21st century! Or at least they will have done when the Trustees have found their way around their mobile phones and the manageress and book-keeper have become computer literate! They are all working on it!

The Internet opened up a brand new world for The Bible House and orders were now coming in from abroad. Of course that was not without its problems. When seven hundred pounds worth of Bibles went missing on their way to Asylum Down Roundabout, Asylum Down Under, in West Africa, Beryl Johnson was forced to rely on telephone calls, e-mails, faxs and the postal service to track them down. In the end, if it hadn't been for the amazing coincidence, that a friend of one of the Trustees actually lived in a town near Asylum Down Under, and was able to help them in their search, the books may never have been found.

Business was also faring well at home in Pilgrim Street. The H.M.S.O. Department in the basement continued to supply the community of Newcastle upon Tyne and surrounding areas with anything they wanted to know about Health and Safety, Government publications, British Standards, education or law. The Children's Department on the first floor, that light airy room with its big window overlooking the Odeon cinema, was always a delight to browsers. There was a large and varied selection of Children's Bibles and colourful story books as well as Christening gifts, jewellery, Sunday School material, C.Ds and tapes, ornaments and novelties within pocket money range. The ground floor, as well as selling a wide range of Bibles and theological books, also benefited from the expanding interest being shown in Christian biographies and autobiographies, teaching and self-help books, daily readings, magazines and newspapers. Cards for all occasions were also very popular.

One significant change for the beneficiaries, was that all surplus profits now went to the Bible Society alone. Entrusted with all this business were the Trustees who still retained their monthly, Friday morning meeting.

The first two Trustees arrived one particular Friday morning.

'Good morning.' they greeted Betty.

'Good morning.' she replied.

Both men made for the stairway leading to the Committee Room when they both sensed a distinct aroma of cooking coming from the basement. Before ascending the stairs they glanced at each other, smiled and said, 'Hoppy's pasty!', almost in unison.

They were followed a few minutes later by Mr Peter Firth. Peter's father, Gordon Firth had been a trustee when Mrs Quick had been manageress. A sensitive, quiet man with white hair and a beard that almost, but not quite, hid a cheery smile.

'Good morning.' he said softly.

'Good morning Mr Firth,' Betty replied.

He was about to walk upstairs when he noticed the gentleman in a cheap suit, using The Bible House telephone and talking to someone rather loudly. Catching the man's eye, he smiled pleasantly. Mr Ridley was well known to The Bible House.

Mr David Kilner noticed neither the man on the telephone nor the smell of hot pies from the basement as he breezed into the shop.

'Good morning ladies!' he called cheerily.

Mr Peter Morley followed at a more leisurely pace but then age allows that privilege. There was time for him to savour the smell of Hoppy's pasty from the basement and give the man on the telephone a nod of acknowledgement.

The Trustees meeting started in the usual manner with prayer. It was a good way to start any meeting. The silence allowed their busy minds to be stilled and the opportunity to bring before God the work of The Bible House and to ask for his help and guidance.

There were a number of matters to discuss on the agenda that morning but somehow they ended up discussing Hoppy, Mr Ridley and the number of people who'd entered the shop recently seeking help with personal problems. The majority of these had been referred to clergy, ministers or to the "Listening Post," at Brunswick Chapel.

'There's always been more to The Bible House than just selling books.' Mr Peter Morley said. 'And I should imagine every manager and every

Trustee going back to 1864, would agree with that view.'

His comments stuck in Beryl's mind for the rest of the meeting, so much so that after the Trustees had left, she found herself in the attic rummaging through the old files and folders for the Minutes of the meetings back in 1864. She unearthed the big picture of the Queen that Hoppy had loved so much and another one of Dr. Billy Graham, preacher and evangelist. Eventually she found the Minutes that she was looking for, hidden in the corner with an old Christmas Nativity scene, where the three kings were all headless and the stable roof had holes in it.. She blew the thick layer of dust off the top book and opened it.

Written by Mr Ephraim Lister in his most beautifully styled handwriting, in pen and ink, these were the Minutes of the first Trustees Meeting of The Bible and Tract Depot held on November 18th, 1864. Present at that meeting had been some eminent businessmen of Newcastle upon Tyne: Mr Thomas Bainbridge, Mr Henry Richardson, Mr Angus, Mr Fenwick, Mr Alexander, Mr Joseph Mather and Mr Pumphrey. They represented various strands of commerce and engineering but the factor which brought them together had been a common vision to promote the gospel of Jesus Christ through the supply of tracts, Bibles and other good quality books, to the poorer people of the area.

Time seemed to stand still as the manageress of the present stepped into the shoes of her predecessors. She read about their worries for the shop and their problems with the staff and the premises. The lives and deaths of the Trustees and those who had worked closely with them to ensure this good work continued, were all identified in the pages. It wasn't until Hazel knocked on the door that she surfaced from her books.

'It's closing time - and you're covered in dust.' Hazel said with a smile.

'I know.' Beryl replied softly. Somehow she didn't want to let go of the dear people into whose shoes she had stepped. She glanced at her watch. 'I'll be with you in a moment.' She stood up, dusted her skirt, then carefully picking up the Minute Books carried them downstairs to her office. She felt too drawn to Mr Ephraim Lister and Miss Margaret Wilson, to leave them in the attic.

The staff had already left when Beryl locked her office door. Thoughtfully she walked down the stairs to the empty Children's Department. She stood looking out of the large windows for what seemed ages. Outside the rush hour was well underway. Buses pulled up in front of The Bible House, laden with commuters leaving the city after their daily work. How had they gone home in Mr Ephraim Lister's day? Walked? Horse and carriage? A small queue was already forming outside the Odeon Cinema for the early evening films and people wandered in and out of the Police Station further down the street. It was hard to believe that Mr Ephraim Lister and Miss Margaret Wilson, began the work of The Bible House on that very spot and that the managers and manageresses before her had gazed up and down Pilgrim Street just like she was doing now.

Silently she made her way down to check the basement. It was all in order. She knew it would be as she had a conscientious staff that could be relied upon. On her way up to the ground floor she noted that the main shop was neat and tidy, every shelf filled with colourful books and Bibles. The window display had been rearranged that very morning.

Beryl Johnson stood with her hand on the door handle, reluctant to leave. For the first time in her few short years as manageress she sensed and understood the deep love and dedication which had been passed down by managers and manageresses before her.

'It's like passing on a blessing.' she whispered to the shop and then she smiled, for as she closed the door she could have sworn she heard Ephraim Lister say, 'It is!'